Electrical Safety and Protection

Contributor:

Alan W. Stanfield
    Electrical Instructor
    Southern Crescent Technical College
    Griffin, Georgia

John Cadick
    Cadick Corporation
    Garland, TX

Kurt Eisenach, B.E.E.
    Adjunct Faculty
    Rainy River Community College
    International Falls, Minnesota

Jay F. Hooper
    Industrial Continuing Education Author
    Freeu
    Salisbury, NC
    Curriculum Instructor
    DCCC
    Lexington, NC

Editor:

Linda Warner

Graphic Design:

Robert A. Ravelo

Schoolcraft
P U B L I S H I N G

A division of
Telemedia, Inc.

Table of Contents

Chapter One

Electrical Hazards

The Importance of Electrical Safety

1.01 Approximately 1100 people die from electric shock each year in the United States. During your daily routine, you are probably exposed to many potentially dangerous situations involving electricity. Modern life depends on electricity to run machinery, to provide heat and light, and to do many of the jobs people takes for granted. Handled with care and respect, electricity is safe and useful, but when handled carelessly, it can be a killer.

1.02 Ignorance of safety regulations is no excuse for violating them. In fact, you can be fired from a job for doing so. If you are unsure about the meaning of a rule or how to follow a procedure, ask your instructor or supervisor for help.

1.03 Keep in mind that accidents seldom "just happen." In most cases, they are the result of unsafe acts rather than unsafe conditions. Common causes include fatigue, stress, carelessness, or ignorance. If you have an accident while on the job, notify your supervisor and the plant medical department. You should also report any unsafe condition or near-accident promptly.

The Electric Circuit

1.04 Many of you are probably familiar with the theory of electricity. Some of you, however, might benefit from a review of some basic principles. The following paragraphs cover points that are important to your understanding of electrical safety.

1.05 Electricity flows through a conducting path in much the same way that water flows through a pipe. This path is called a *circuit. Current* is the

Fig. 1-1. Grounded electric circuit

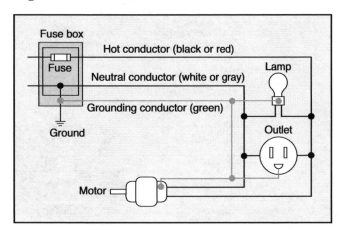

amount of charge carried by the electrons flowing past a given point in a given time. Energy is required to move the charge through a conductor. The energy that moves the charge comes from a generator or battery. The source does not produce any electrons. It only supplies the energy to move the electrons that are present—much as pressure supplies the energy in a piping system. As the electrons move through a conductor, they encounter resistance and lose energy. The loss in energy, per unit of charge, is measured in *volts* (V).

1.06   In a simple electric circuit, electricity is delivered to a lamp or other device through a wire, often called the *hot wire*, and leaves through a wire that is connected to the ground. These two wires complete the circuit. A third wire, called a *grounding conductor*, connects the metal housing of the device to the ground to prevent it from being energized. Electrical wires are coded by standard colors of their insulation. A hot wire is either black or red. A neutral wire is white or gray. The grounding wire is green or green with a yellow stripe. Figure 1-1 shows these wire colors in a simple circuit.

1.07   An open circuit cannot conduct current. When you turn off a switch or disconnect a line cord, you create a gap in the conducting path of the circuit. When the gap is closed, the circuit is said to be closed. If your body closes the gap, you become part of the circuit.

1.08   Every complete path in a circuit can conduct current. The amount of current depends on how much resistance is in each path of the circuit and on the voltage of the source. Electric current is measured in amperes (A) and milliamperes (mA). A milliampere is one one-thousandth of an ampere.

1.09   A circuit that supplies 2 A to a soldering iron and 5 A to a grinder must supply a total of 7 A. The current is divided as shown in Fig. 1-2. If an electric heater is added to the circuit and it draws an additional 10 A, the total current increases to 17 A. The larger current due to the additional load will blow a 15 A fuse in the circuit.

1.10   Electric circuits are described by their voltages and by their current capacity. The most common voltages for homes are 120 V for lights and small appliances, and 208 or 240 V for electric ranges, clothes dryers, and air conditioners. The most common voltages for industrial plants are 120, 208 and 240 V for small appliances and 480 V for motors and other equipment. Other voltages are also used in plants.

1.11   The 120 V circuits usually have current capacities of either 15 or 20 A, although 30 or 40 A circuits are possible if large enough wires are used. The 240 V circuits usually have capacities of 20 to 70 A. The 480 V circuits have capacities of 20 to hundreds of amperes. In all circuits, the size of the wire used depends on the current the circuit must carry. The wire size does not depend on the voltage of the circuit.

Electric Shock

1.12   When working with any electric circuit, you are always exposed to the potential for shock. Some shock hazards are obvious—assuming a circuit is dead without testing (or testing it with your finger to see if it is live), using an electric tool that gives you a tingle when you touch it, or using a device with a frayed cord or a cracked plug. Other shock hazards, however, are not so obvious. Avoiding shock hazards requires regular inspections, good preventive maintenance, and common sense. You should have a healthy respect for all electrical equipment. Always follow safety procedures and use the required personal protective equipment.

1.13   Electric shock occurs when current passes through the body. The effect of the current on the human body depends on several factors:

* the amount of current passing through the body

* the path of the current through the body

* the length of time the body conducts the current.

Secondary factors include age, size, physical condition, and the frequency of the current (ac is slightly more dangerous than dc).

Fig. 1-2. Every complete path can conduct current

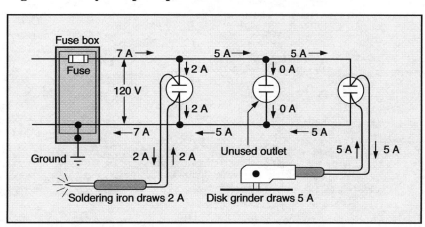

Table 1-1. Effect of alternating electric current on the human body

Milliamperes	Effect
1 or less	Shock probably is not even felt.
1 to 3	Shock is felt, but is not painful.
3 to 10	Shock is painful. Individual can let go at will. Muscular control is not lost.
10 to 20	Some individuals cannot let go at will because muscular control is lost.
20 to 75	Individual cannot let go. Breathing is difficult or impossible.
75 to 4000	Possible ventricular fibrillation of the heart, causing death. Severe muscular contraction and nerve damage.
Over 4000	Possible heart paralysis and/or severe burns.

1.14   You can receive a shock or burn from any common electric circuit. The current needed to cause a serious or fatal injury is a small fraction of an ampere. An ordinary 120 V circuit can deliver 20 A of current or more before the circuit breaker trips or the fuse blows. This current is many times the amount that can kill a person.

1.15   When current passes through the human body, the effect can range from a mild tingle to death. Even a small and harmless shock can startle you and make you pull back suddenly, sometimes striking something or falling from a height. An electric shock is particularly dangerous when you are unable to let go of the source of the shock and the current tightens your chest muscles so that you cannot breathe. Other results of shock are burns and severe internal bleeding.

1.16   Electric current affects different body parts differently. For example, 30 mA can paralyze the diaphragm, making breathing impossible. A current as low as 75 mA can affect the rhythm of the heart. Current can also cause severe burns. Table 1-1 is a list of the kinds of damage small currents can cause in the human body.

1.17   Most fatal shocks occur when the current passes through or near the heart. If the path is through both arms, or through an arm and a leg, as shown in Fig. 1-3, the current passes through the chest and near the heart. A current of 100 mA that passes through the heart for only one-third of a second can cause *ventricular fibrillation*, a condition that causes the heart to flutter uselessly and blood circulation to stop. Unless the heart returns to its normal beat and blood flow resumes quickly, the brain is damaged

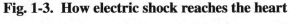

Fig. 1-3. How electric shock reaches the heart

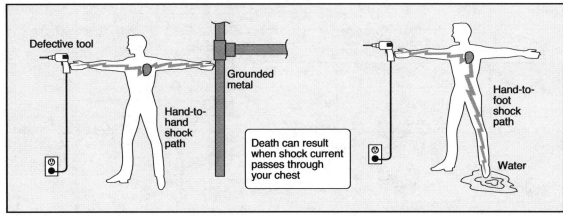

and a short time later the victim dies. Restoring a normal heartbeat usually requires immediate use of special equipment by a trained medical technician. Such assistance is often not available soon enough to help the victim.

1.18   Although shocks over 200 mA are not necessarily fatal, these more severe shocks cause the chest muscles to contract so hard that they stop the heart completely. If this severe shock does not last too long, first aid measures sometimes can be used to restart the heart.

1.19   If a person becomes the victim of electric shock, prompt and proper first aid can mean the difference between life and death. Sufficient circulation can sometimes be maintained by heart compression, which should always be supported with mouth-to-mouth resuscitation. This combination of treatments is commonly known as *cardiopulmonary resuscitation* (CPR). First aid and CPR are covered in Chapter Three.

1.20   Your body can become part of an electric circuit in the following ways:

- when you contact the hot and neutral conductors at the same time. In this situation, your body is like a light bulb filament or the windings in a motor. It becomes a current path between the wires.

- when you contact a hot conductor while you are in contact with the ground or a grounded structure. This unintentional grounding is described in more detail in Chapter Four.

- when you contact two hot wires with different voltages on them.

- when a ground fault occurs. This situation occurs when a hot conductor touches the metal housing or frame, causing it to become energized. If you are touching the metal housing when it becomes energized and another part of your body is in contact with ground, you will receive a shock.

1.21   The path of least resistance always conducts the most current. Table 1-2, on the following page, gives some typical electrical resistances. As you can see from Table 1-2, electrical resistance varies widely between materials and within the human body.

1.22   Three factors determine electrical resistance:

- **Physical size of the substance.** Resistance varies directly with length, and inversely with cross-sectional area.

Table 1-2. Electrical resistance of common materials

Material	Resistance in ohms	Current produced by 120 V
Wood 1 in. dry 1 in. wet	200,000 to 200 million 2000 to 100,000	0.6 to 0.0006 mA 60 to 1.2 mA
Metal 1000 ft No. 10 copper wire	1	120 A
Human body Dry skin Damp skin Wet skin Hand-to-foot Ear-to-ear	100,000 to 600,000 Down to 1000 Down to 150 400 to 600 100	1.2 to 0.2 mA Up to 120 mA Up to 800 mA 300 to 200 mA 1200 mA

- **Properties of the substance.** Some substances conduct electricity easily. Others offer great resistance to the flow of electrons.

- **Purity of the substance.** Pure water does not conduct electricity. Small amounts of dissolved minerals and salts, however, make water a good conductor. Perspiration contains salts and minerals, and therefore increases the ability of the human body to conduct electricity.

1.23 Dry, nonmetallic materials generally resist electricity well. However, these same materials become better electrical conductors if they become damp. This rule applies to your body as well. Dry skin has greater electrical resistance than wet skin. Therefore your body will conduct less current if your skin is dry. However, if a body becomes part of a high-voltage circuit, the skin may be punctured. The current is then limited only by the internal resistance of the body, and the current is much higher because of lower resistance.

1.24 When the skin is dry, the shock from a 120 V circuit might be less than 1 mA. Consequently, it produces little or no sensation. But even a small amount of perspiration or moisture greatly reduces the skin's resistance. When skin is moist, a 120 V circuit can produce a deadly shock. A person standing in water or leaning against a wet object can receive a shock of 800 mA—far above the lethal level.

1.25 You can take several precautions to guard against electric shock:

- *Insulation* provides electrical separation between you and the conductor.

- *Grounding* provides a low-resistance electrical path to earth.

- *GFCIs* detect current leaking to ground and turn off the circuit.

- *Lockout* prevents a circuit from being energized while you are working on it.

These and other safeguards are covered in detail in later chapterss.

Electric Arc

1.26   An *electric arc* is a discharge of electricity through a gas. Electric arcing most often occurs when two conductors in an electric circuit are separated. For an arc to form, enough electrical energy must be available to maintain the current through the separation. Air itself cannot conduct current. It is vaporized material at the arc terminal and ionized particles of air that actually conduct the current. The mixture of materials through which the arc travels is called *plasma*.

1.27   Electric arcs are extremely hot and can cause serious burns. They can ignite clothing and cause fatal burns from a distance of several feet. The closer you are to the arc and the longer you are exposed to it, the more severe your injuries will be.

1.28   Electric arcing can also cause an increase in pressure that can cause violent explosions and send bullet-like fragments and molten metal flying. These blasts can be so powerful that they can blow out walls. Eye damage, severe burns, and many other injures can be the direct result of these explosions. Whenever there is the possibility of an electric arc, you should:

- wear appropriate face, eye, and ear protection

- wear arc rated (AR) clothing

- maintain as much distance as possible between yourself and the potential source of the arc.

Basic Rules of Electrical Safety

1.29   To avoid the hazards of electric shock and arcing, safety must be planned into every job. If you are not sure how to perform a certain task (or how to perform it safely), ask your supervisor or an experienced fellow worker. Never take chances that could endanger you or others.

1.30 The Occupational Safety and Health Administration (OSHA) has established procedures or *standards* for working safely with or near electrical equipment and wiring. OSHA standards differ from all other industry standards in that they are enforceable under United States law. All workers should follow these procedures, whether or not they are qualified persons. The *National Electrical Code* (*NEC*) defines a *qualified person* as "one familiar with the construction and operation of the equipment and the hazards involved." All electrical installation and repair work in a plant should be performed by, or under the direction of, a qualified person and should follow *NEC* installation and design standards.

1.31 **Clothing.** Wearing the proper clothing and protective equipment when working around electricity can help you work safely. Some basic rules follow:

- Do not wear rings, watches, or any metal jewelry or ornaments. Not only can these articles come into contact with electric circuits, they can become caught in moving machinery.

- Wear a nonconducting, plastic, ANSI Class G or E hard hat (formerly Class A or B).

- Wear safety glasses.

- Wear shoes with nonconducting rubber soles.

- Wear heavy cotton clothing. In the event of an explosion or fire, clothing made of polyester or other synthetic fabrics can melt onto your skin and cause serious burns.

- Even if the power is locked out, wear protective equipment (insulating gloves and sleeve covers) if there is any chance of it becoming inadvertently re-energized. To protect yourself against arcing, wear flash/flame resistant clothing, a flash suit, eye protection, and a face shield.

1.32 **Equipment.** The precautions that follow apply to equipment and tools used on or near electric circuits:

- Use the proper devices and tools for the job. Examine safety devices before using them to make sure they are in good condition. Examine all electric power tools and other electrical equipment for signs of damage or wear. Never use faulty power tools. When tools or their cords are damaged, replace them at once.

- Use insulated tools rather than non-insulated tools when working on electrical equipment. Use only intrinsically safe or explosion-proof tools and hand lamps in hazardous locations. In metal tanks, use 6 or 12 V equipment.

- Keep all electric machinery free of dust, dirt, oil, and stray tools and parts. Do not store your lunch, tools, or anything else in switch boxes.

- Where appropriate, make sure all equipment meets the requirements of a recognized testing laboratory. Underwriters Laboratory (UL) and Factory Mutual (FM) are the two best-known certifying agencies.

- Never overload a circuit, even when all equipment is laboratory-certified.

- Do not clean or repair machinery while it is in motion without specific directions from your supervisor, or unless precautions have been taken to allow you to do the work safely.

- Do not use metal ladders near electricity.

1.33 **Enclosures.** Keep electrical enclosure doors secured and locked. Industrial and commercial enclosure doors are often hinged and held closed with a latch that allows for the use of a padlock. In addition to the latch, equipment doors are sometimes held closed with screws or bolts that help hold the door closed if an internal explosion occurs. For your safety, it is important that door screws be tightened when equipment is energized, as shown in Fig. 1-4.

1.34 Circuit breakers or disconnect switches should be opened or closed only when equipment doors are secured (closed and bolted). When you open or close a circuit with a circuit breaker or disconnect, there is a possibility that a circuit fault might exist, causing an overload, arcing, and/or explosion. Therefore, when opening or closing a circuit, be alert, wear protective equipment, stand to the side of the switch as much as possible, and operate the switch with a quick positive motion.

1.35 **Wiring.** Wires with damaged or deteriorating insulation must be replaced. Only in an emergency should a wire be wrapped temporarily with electrical tape. As a general rule, leave wiring jobs for a qualified electrician.

Fig. 1-4. Electrical enclosure door

Fig. 1-5. Lock out power before working on equipment

1.36 **Water.** Water and electricity make a deadly combination. Check your work area for puddles and wet surfaces. Do not energize electrical equipment when it is wet or damp with condensation. If equipment is stored outdoors in cold weather and brought indoors for use, make sure that all condensation has evaporated from the insulation before the equipment is used. If electrical equipment is wet, dry it in the sun or in a warm, dry room. If heat is applied for drying, the temperature should be limited to 200°F. De-energize all electrical equipment in the area before attempting to extinguish a fire with water. Do not try to put out an electrical fire with water. Use only an extinguisher designed for electrical (Class C) fires.

1.37 **Lockout.** If the unexpected start-up of equipment is likely to endanger people, you must lock out power to the equipment. When equipment is to be worked on, each worker involved should have his or her own padlock to lock out power. If you will be working on a motor control center, for example, use a lockout device like the one in Fig. 1-5. You must have a lock for every power source supplying the electrical equipment. Figure 1-6 shows two possible lockout locations. Lockout/tagout procedures are covered in greater detail in Chapter Three.

1.38 Even when the power is locked out, wear protective equipment and use insulated tools. To prevent an accident, treat dead circuits as though they are live. Test every circuit at the point where you will be exposed before starting work. Alert all persons who might be endangered by the work you are doing.

Hazardous Electrical Locations

1.39 If flammable materials or explosive gases are normally present near electrical equipment, special safety measures are needed. In these situations, explosion-proof or intrinsically safe equipment is installed to minimize the hazard. Examples of typical hazardous electrical locations include petrochemical plants, oil-based paint manufacturing facilities, mines, sewers, and grain storage facilities.

1.40 *Explosion-proof enclosures* for equipment can contain sparks, high temperatures, and explosions so that the atmosphere outside the enclosure cannot be ignited. For example, gasoline fumes might leak into

Fig. 1-6. Lock out every power source

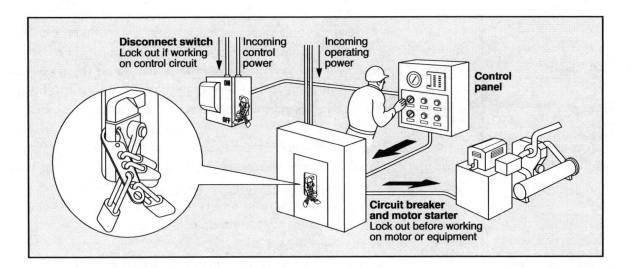

an equipment enclosure and cause an internal explosion. With an explosion-proof enclosure, however, the explosion is contained inside the enclosure, and no external damage results from the detonation of the explosive atmosphere.

1.41   Some electrical equipment is referred to as *intrinsically safe* because it is designed to release only low levels of electrical energy. This kind of equipment cannot cause an explosion or fire of the specific hazardous material.

1.42   Explosion-proof and intrinsically safe electrical equipment is usually designed, selected, and installed for a particular hazardous condition that is expected at a location. This equipment must be installed, used, and maintained with care, or the hazard will remain and the equipment will not be safe to use. If an accidental leak or spill occurs during use, for example, the hazardous material can escape into unexpected areas where general-purpose electrical equipment is installed. Special precautions then must be taken to turn off the electric power without igniting the liquid, gas, dust, or other material.

Additional Hazards

1.43   **Confined spaces.** A *confined space* is an area that has poor natural ventilation and is not designed for occupancy by workers on a continuous basis. Although work in a confined space is not a common part of the workday for most electrical maintenance workers, deaths involving confined spaces occur all too frequently. The information in this chapter offers only brief guidelines. The full OSHA guidelines are much more extensive. As a general rule, never enter a confined space without following the complete OSHA required procedure.

1.44   The most important safety consideration for workers in a confined space is the atmosphere within the space. Not only must there be enough oxygen to support life, but the atmosphere must not be flammable, toxic, or explosive. Although testing the air in confined spaces is important, mechanical ventilation is also needed to maintain a safe atmosphere.

1.45   **Lifting.** When performing electrical work, it might be necessary for you to do some heavy lifting. If at all possible, use material-handling equipment. Use your muscles only as a last resort. Make sure you know your own limits and know how to lift safely. Many workers have been seriously injured while lifting too much or lifting improperly.

1.46   **Fire.** Everyone should take every precaution possible to prevent fires. Fires can be started by burning cigarettes, combustible trash, careless use of matches, improperly installed electrical equipment, or improper storage of oily rags or gasoline.

1.47   Become acquainted with the location and operation of all fire-fighting equipment within your work area. In case of a fire, first consider the safety of the people in the plant. Next, make sure you report the fire. Only after everyone is safe and the fire has been reported should you become concerned about saving property. Do not attempt to save property if doing so will endanger your life.

1.48   **Falls.** Falls from any height can be dangerous. Working surfaces covered with dust, oil, or grease are dangerous at ground level. Your job might require you to work on walls, ceilings, roofs, or other elevated areas. Falls can be far more dangerous at raised elevations. Falls rank second only to motor-vehicle accidents as the most frequent cause of fatal injuries in the United States.

1.49   When working at heights, you must consider not only your own safety but the safety of others. Dropped tools or materials can do great damage below. Place signs and barricades to warn others of the danger of falling objects.

1.50   Do not overreach when you are on a ladder. Get down and move the ladder to a better position, if necessary. Reaching too far to the side can cause a portable ladder to shift and fall. Keep your hips in position over the ladder so that your center of gravity is always over its base. Never use a metal ladder when working with electricity. Use extreme care when handling or using any ladder near electricity.

1.51   **Moving parts.** At some time, you will probably be required to work near moving machinery. Become familiar with the safety rules involving the guarding of moving parts. Make sure that all guards are in place before you start work. Barriers are placed around a job for your protection. Respect them. If you must work near the moving equipment, turn off the machine and lock out the power.

1.52   **Noise.** Because noise seldom causes pain, most people do not realize just how sensitive their ears are to loud noises. Noise is measured in decibels (dB). In a very quiet room, a person with good hearing can just barely hear a sound measuring 1 dB. In the average factory, the noise level measures 80 to 85 dB. You can stand this level of noise for eight hours without damaging your hearing. But if you work longer hours or if the noise level is greater than 85 dB, you need to protect your hearing. A typical punch press measures over 100 dB. At 110 dB, sound becomes painful to the normal ear.

1.53   Earplugs and earmuffs are commonly used to protect hearing in noisy work areas. Some earplugs are disposable and are made of fiber or foam that fits into the ear canal. Reusable plugs are made of soft rubber or plastic. Earmuffs are designed to fit over the entire ear. The outsides of the earmuffs are hard, cup-shaped shells. They are lined with material that absorbs sound and sealed around the edges with a soft, cushioning material. They are mounted on an adjustable headband that fits over the head (or under the chin when worn with a safety hat).

Chapter Two

Electrical Safety Equipment

Work Clothes

2.01   For electrical workers, good quality work clothing that fits well is the basic requirement. Make certain you wear long sleeves to protect your arms. A heavy fabric is best, as it offers some protection from heat as well as from cuts and scrapes. However, you should avoid loose-fitting clothing near moving machinery. The clothing could become entangled in the moving parts and result in serious injury.

2.02   When working around electricity, never wear clothing made of nylon, polyester, or certain other synthetic fabrics. In the presence of intense heat, like that from an electric arc, these fabrics can melt onto your skin. All-cotton clothing is a better choice, as it will burn away in the presence of intense heat.

2.03   A still better choice for working in areas where electric arcing is possible is a cotton fabric that has been chemically treated to make it flame resistant. Although these fabrics resist sparks and open flames and are self-extinguishing, they offer only moderate protection from heat. The best fabric choices are Nomex®, PBI®, or similar fabrics. These fabrics do not melt or catch fire and they offers excellent thermal protection. Ask your supervisor which level of protection is right for you in the work you are doing.

2.04   All clothing worn in the workplace requires periodic cleaning. Ask your employer how your work clothing should be cleaned and how often cleaning should be done. It is important to follow manufacturer's instructions to preserve thermal and fire-retardant properties of some

®NOMEX is a registered trademark of the E. I. Dupont de Nemours Company
®PBI is a registered trademark of Hoescht Celanese Corp.

clothing. Some working conditions might require that your work clothing be left at work for professional cleaning.

Personal Protective Equipment

2.05   The workplace can present hazards not normally encountered elsewhere. Some of the control measures for these hazards depend solely on the worker. These control measures are called *personal protective equipment* (PPE). PPE is often used along with other safety control measures so that you are still protected if the other measures fail. Examples include hart hats, safety glasses, gloves, and respirators.

2.06   Government safety regulations place several responsibilities regarding personal protective equipment on employers. Your employer is responsible for:

- identifying the PPE to be worn in the workplace

- ensuring that the appropriate PPE is worn

- ensuring that only approved PPE is used

- ensuring that PPE is cleaned and maintained properly

- training employees in the purpose, limitations, and proper use of PPE.

2.07   You too have responsibilities regarding PPE. You are responsible for:

- inspecting all required PPE for cleanliness and proper function before you use it

- wearing the PPE correctly

- using all the PPE required for the task

- reporting any defects in the equipment.

It is important to remember that your protection depends on proper use of the required equipment.

2.08   Manufacturers of protective equipment provide instructions on how the equipment should be used and maintained as well as a description of the protection it provides. Read and follow the instructions carefully and know the limitations of the equipment.

Special Body Protection

2.09   To protect you and your work clothes, special garments, aprons, and sleeve protectors must sometimes be worn over your work clothes. This protective gear can be made various materials, each of which provides a specific kind of protection and has certain limitations. For example, most special body protection devices used in the workplace to protect you from extreme heat and flame do not provide protection from chemicals. Garments designed for chemical protection usually do not provide protection from extreme heat or flame.

2.10   The hazards of a particular task determine what body protection material, design, and construction are needed. Many kinds of protective garments are used in industry, ranging from flame-retardant garments used in welding operations and electrical work to fully encapsulating chemical suits used to handle highly toxic or unknown chemicals. It is important to remember that the hazards of a particular job determine the special body protection required—there is no single garment or device that can protect you in all situations.

Fig. 2-1. Flash suit

2.11   When performing electrical work where the danger of electric arc is great, you should wear a *flash suit* made of flame-retardant material, as shown in Fig. 2-1. Follow your company's rules concerning when it is to be worn. It might need to be combined with additional eye, hand, and head protection. These suits are rated by degrees of continuous ambient temperature. If a suit's continuous ambient rating is 450°F, its short term rating is much higher.

Foot Protection

2.12   Because about one in ten disabling injuries to industrial workers is to the feet and toes, a wide variety of protective footwear is available. For example, in areas where there is a danger of falling objects, safety shoes with steel toe boxes and metatarsal guards are common. Flexible metal insoles prevent sharp pieces of metal from entering the sole of a safety shoe and piercing the foot. Workers who must stand or work on hot surfaces wear special soles that do not conduct heat. In wet areas, waterproof shoes or pullover boots help keep the feet dry. On slippery or oily surfaces, nonskid soles help prevent slips and falls.

2.13   When working with electricity, specialized foot protection is sometimes required. Electrical workers often wear shoes stitched and cemented without nails to reduce electrical conductivity. These shoes also have an insulating layer sandwiched within the sole. Check with your supervisor to determine what kind of shoe is right for the work you do.

WARNING

It is extremely important that you inspect rubber protective equipment carefully before using it. Tears, holes, and cracks, can destroy its insulating properties. Rubber gloves should be air tested before each use. To perform the air test, the glove should be inflated, visually examined for holes, and held close to the face to listen and feel for air leaks.

Gloves

2.14   Gloves are commonly used in the workplace to protect hands against cuts, puncture wounds, chemicals, and hot and cold temperature extremes. Just as with special body-protection devices, there are many materials used to manufacture gloves. Glove selection depends on the hazards associated with the job. There is no single glove that can provide protection against all hazards. In fact, sometimes two gloves must be worn at the same time to protect against all hazards involved in a particular job.

2.15   When working with electrical equipment, especially if you could come into contact with an energized conductor, wear leather gloves over rubber gloves. Glove combinations, like the ones shown in Fig. 2-2, are made especially for this purpose. Never wear one without the other. The rubber offers electrical insulation between you and the conductor. The leather protects the rubber from holes and tears. Sometimes these combination gloves include a cotton liner to make the gloves more comfortable.

2.16   When working in close quarters, in locations where your arms might come into contact with an energized conductor, rubber sleeve covers are sometimes needed to protect your arms from accidental contact

Fig. 2-2. Combination gloves for electrical work

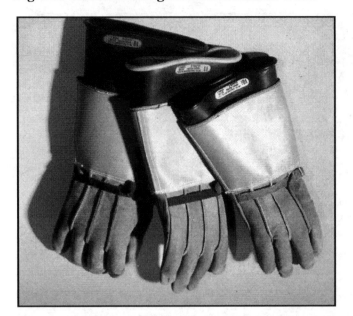

Fig. 2-3. Hard hat

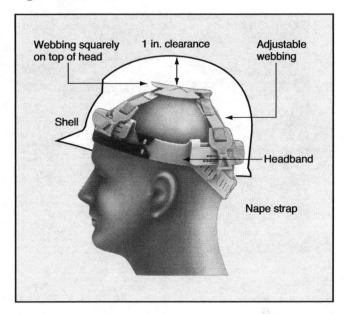

with energized conductors. Rubber sleeve covers are available in several voltage classes, styles, sizes, and materials. Your supervisor can help you choose the one that is right for you.

Head Protection

2.17   One of the most common pieces of personal protective equipment is the hard hat. Once made of metal, today's hard hats are made of reinforced plastic, which can offer the advantage of electrical insulation. They have an adjustable headband and suspension webbing, as shown in Fig. 2-3. The webbing should provide a 1 in. clearance between your head and the top of the shell. Without this space, a blow from a falling object would be transmitted directly to the skull and could cause serious injury. The webbing also allows air to circulate under the shell. In warm weather or warm work areas, this circulating air helps keep you cool. In cold weather, a liner inside the hat will help keep your head and ears warm.

2.18   Check your hat each time you wear it. Examine the shell for dents, cracks, or holes. Inspect the webbing for loose, torn, or defective straps. Do not use the hat if you see anything wrong. Remember, it is the webbing that takes the impact and protects your head. Avoid using harsh cleansers or solvents to clean your hard hat. Instead use only soap and warm water.

2.19   All hard hats are designed to protect your head from the impact of falling objects and other blows. When working with electricity, however,

Fig. 2-4. Safety glasses and goggles

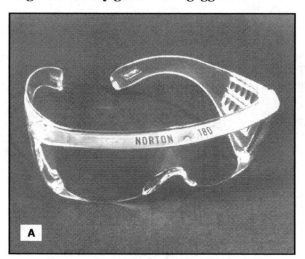

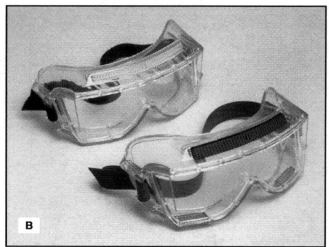

you must choose a hard hat that also provides electrical insulation. The American National Standards Institute (ANSI) has classified hard hats into three classes. Class G hard hats (formerly Class A) reduce the hazard of contact with low-voltage (up to 2200 V phase-to-ground) conductors. Class E hard hats (formerly Class B) are intended for high-voltage (20,000 V phase-to-ground) protection. Class C hard hats offer no electrical protection. Make sure to select a hard hat that provides the appropriate electrical protection. You should wear a Class G or E hard hat anytime there is a possibility that you could be exposed to mechanical blows or to electric shock, arc, or blast.

Eye Protection

2.20   Eye protection might seem to be a nuisance. You can probably think of several excuses for not wearing safety glasses or goggles, but an excuse will not prevent blindness. Many electrical workers have suffered severe, permanent eye damage from accidents that occurred while they were not wearing eye protection. All electrical workers should wear eye protection at all times on the job.

2.21   **Safety glasses.** Industrial safety glasses have stronger lenses and stronger frames than everyday eyeglasses. Safety glasses will not shatter as easily as regular glasses if something hits them. When side shields are added, as shown in Fig. 2-4A, the glasses also protect your eyes from the sides. Make sure that your safety glasses fit you properly. Wear them up against your face, not down on your nose.

2.22   Safety glasses are also available as prescription glasses. In fact, the only prescription eyeglasses that can be worn in an industrial setting are those approved by ANSI. For additional protection, you can wear prescription safety glasses under safety goggles. Do not wear contact lenses without first checking with your supervisor or safety officer. They can be dangerous in the plant.

2.23   Eyeglass lenses that change their tint with changes in light level are not suitable for use in the plant. They take a minute or so to adjust, and during that time you will not be able to see well. If tinted glasses are required on your job, ordinary sunglasses are not adequate. Make sure to use glasses with the required protection.

2.24   **Safety goggles.** When something can come at you fast (an electric arc, for example) or can splash in your eyes, you must wear safety goggles. Often you cannot see a liquid, spark, or piece of metal flying at you in time to react. Safety goggles offer better protection than safety glasses, because they prevent dust, chips, and liquids from reaching your eyes from any direction. Some goggles offer UV protection, which is important in case of an electric arc. Some typical safety goggles are shown in Fig. 2-4B.

2.25   The need for safety goggles varies from plant to plant and from work area to work area. But the reason for wearing them is always the same—to protect your eyes from liquid splashes, flying objects, particles in the air, and intense light. In some plants, you are required to wear eye protection whenever you are in certain areas, even if you are not actively working.

2.26   **First aid for eyes.** If foreign particles enter your eyes, do not attempt to remove them. Instead, consult a doctor immediately. Do not rub an injured eye, as this action can cause additional damage. There is one kind of eye injury that you should treat immediately on the job, however—an injury caused by chemicals. Strong chemicals act on the eye very rapidly. Such accidents often occur in areas where storage batteries are kept or charged. These chemicals can cause blindness very quickly if they are not rinsed out immediately.

2.27   If your eyes should come in contact with a chemical, you must remove the chemical as quickly as possible. Eyewash fountains like the one shown in Fig. 2-5 should be available in any work area in which this kind of accident could happen. It is a good idea to locate the nearest fountain before you start the job. If an eyewash fountain is not available, you can use a drinking fountain, flowing water from a hose, or even a

Fig. 2-5. Eyewash fountain

simple container of clean water in an emergency. Make sure the container is large enough so you can immerse your face.

2.28   If a chemical is splashed in another worker's eyes, you might need to lead that person to the nearest eyewash fountain. Start applying water immediately and continue for at least 15 minutes until the eyes are thoroughly flushed. Call for medical help. Do not attempt to apply a neutralizer. Any such material should be applied only by a doctor after the eyes have been washed thoroughly with clean water.

2.29   Use these same procedures if a strong chemical comes in contact with your skin. Use an emergency shower immediately. If your clothing becomes soaked by the chemical, remove it at once.

Face Protection

2.30   A face shield protects your face and neck from flying particles. It also provides some protection against injuries from sparks, sprays, and splashes. Face shields are usually made of transparent plastic and can be raised or lowered as required. Face shields are often worn when machine tools are being operated and when liquid chemicals are being handled.

2.31   A face shield alone does not completely protect your eyes, because you might turn your head and allow a spark or splash to reach your eyes. Goggles worn underneath the shield will protect your eyes from this kind of danger. The face shield of a flash suit, like the one shown in Fig. 2-1, will protect your face from molten metal and other flying objects.

Safety Harnesses and Lifelines

2.32   A safety harness can save your life if you fall when climbing or working at heights. The safety harness can limit falls and prevent serious injury. For example, if you are in a high place and slip, a commercially available safety harness limits your fall to only a couple of feet.

2.33   If your job requires you to enter a tank, boiler, or other confined space, a lifeline should be attached to the safety harness. If something goes wrong, the lifeline is your means of rescue. If you are injured or overcome by gases or vapors, you can be pulled to safety by the lifeline. Confined space entry requires a great deal of specialized training. It is mentioned here only to alert you to the potential hazards.

WARNING

Never enter a confined space unless you have received special training.

Respiratory Protection

2.34   Respiratory protection is required for both workers and rescue personnel in a variety of work environments. Although electrical work does not normally require respiratory protection, your job might take you into areas in which respirators must be worn—those containing airborne toxic chemicals and those containing too little oxygen, for example.

2.35   Should you be required to use a respirator, you must receive a great deal of additional training on their selection and use. Some respirators remove dust and other harmful particles but are not effective against vapors and gases. In some situations, the atmosphere in an area does not contain enough oxygen to support life and an oxygen-supplying respirator must be used.

2.36   Before employees use respirators in a facility, OSHA requires that employers have a written respiratory protection program. In addition, employers must provide employees with medical examinations and specialized training. Do not use a respirator unless you are medically qualified to wear one, have received appropriate training, and have had the respirator's fit tested. Deaths have occurred during respirator use because these conditions were not met.

Lockout/Tagout Devices

2.37   To protect yourself and other workers in an area, you must usually lock out and tag the main disconnect switch in the OFF position before working on electrical equipment. Most switch boxes are made so that a padlock can be snapped into place. The lock will prevent the operation of equipment that has been de-energized. The tag identifies the nature of the work in progress and the worker who placed the lock and tag.

2.38   OSHA makes the following requirements regarding tagout devices:

- Tags must clearly identify the employee who applies them. When a tag is attached to an energy-isolating device, it must not be

Fig. 2-6. Lockout/tagout devices

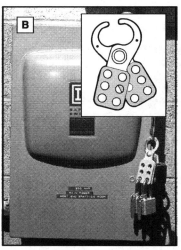

removed except by the person who applied it. Tags should never be bypassed or ignored.

- Tags must be readable and understandable by all employees. They must warn against the hazardous condition that will result if the machine or equipment is energized. Most tags have legends such as DO NOT START, DO NOT OPEN, DO NOT OPERATE, DANGER, etc. An example is shown in Fig. 2-6A.

- Tags must be made of materials that can withstand the environmental conditions in which they will be used.

- Tags must be affixed securely to energy-isolating devices so that they cannot be detached accidentally during use.

2.39   Several padlocks should be available to every electrician in the plant. If several workers are working on a piece of equipment, a multiple-lock device, like the one shown in Fig. 2-6B, should be available so each worker can attach his or her own lock. Leave your padlock in place until you finish the job. Equipment cannot be restarted until all locks have been removed.

2.40   Your lock should be removable only with its matching key, although a master key is sometimes kept for emergency situations. Remember that installation or removal of a padlock involves taking on responsibility. The main power lockout cannot be reopened until all workers have opened their locks and removed them.

2.41   Devices are also available to lock out circuit breakers and wall switches. These devices are screwed on and lock over the switch and screws. An example is shown in Fig. 2-6C.

Fig. 2-7. Barricade tape

Fig. 2-8. Insulated hand tool set

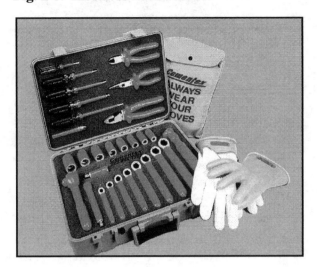

Barricade Tape

2.42   In some cases, it is important to keep nonessential plant personnel out of an area where hazardous electrical work is being performed. This is especially true if the job requires the removal of doors or other guards that would normally offer protection.

2.43   In these situations, you should use plastic barricade tape to mark off the restricted area. The tape should be at least 2 in. wide and, according to OSHA specifications, must be red or yellow in color. The tape should be displayed at a level that is readily visible and should enclose the entire danger area. When you complete your work, make sure to remove the tape. Sample tape is shown in Fig. 2-7.

Electrical Tools

2.44   Although most hand tools do not seem especially hazardous, using the wrong tool or using a tool incorrectly can be dangerous, especially when working with electricity. Anyone working on or near an energized conductor must use insulated tools. These tools are used just like others, but most of the tool is covered with an electrical insulation to protect the worker from the hazards of electric shock or arc.

2.45   Tool maintenance is especially important when working with these tools. Inspect all tools before using them to make sure that they are in good, safe condition. It is especially important that the insulation be undamaged, or the tool's insulating value will be lost. A set of insulated tools is shown in Fig. 2-8.

Fig. 2-9. Hot stick

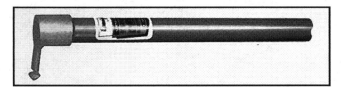

2.46 Another kind of tool you should be aware of the hot stick. *Hot sticks* are tools used by electrical workers to perform tasks or manipulate conductors from a distance. These devices are simply poles made of an insulating material, usually fiberglass. An example is shown in Fig. 2-9. Many models can be fitted with attachments, which allow them to perform a variety of tasks. Attachments include tools and test instruments. If a job situation calls for the use of a hot stick, you should wear protective clothing—at least gloves and eye protection.

Voltage Testers

2.47 A *voltage tester* is a simple device. It tells you whether there is a potential difference between two points, but it does not measure the potential difference. In many cases, you will use it to verify that a system has been de-energized and that there is no potential difference. If you need to know the value of a potential difference, you should use a voltmeter.

Fig. 2-10. Voltage tester

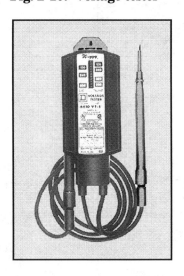

2.48 A commercially available pocket-type voltage tester is shown in Fig. 2-10. The pointer moves when the instrument is connected across an ac source. You can carry it in your tool pouch, where it is available for immediate use. It eliminates the need to carry a delicate voltmeter on the job. The potential-difference scale on the tester has voltage indication for ac on one side of the pointer and for dc on the other side. The ac scale indicates 120-240-480-600 V. The dc scale indicates 125-240-600 V.

Chapter Three

Electrical Safety Procedures

Energy Control

3.01 As an electrical maintenance worker, you should know that servicing an energized piece of equipment is an open invitation to an accident. You should also know, however, that throwing the main switch is not all that is required for safe maintenance. *Energy control* involves not only shutting off electricity but also releasing any stored mechanical, pneumatic, or hydraulic energy that might be present in the equipment. Your goal should be to bring the equipment to a *zero energy state*. This concept will be discussed in detail later in this chapter.

WARNING

Never attempt to make repairs on electrical equipment unless you have the proper training, including training in lockout procedures.

3.02 Your company should have a written plan with instructions for de-energizing each system or piece of equipment. The plan should include the voltage level and short-circuit capabilities of the equipment to be de-energized. This information will define the level of hazard. The plan should include specific instructions for switching, as well as information on the required protective equipment.

3.03 Finally, the plan should include instructions for re-energizing. Re-energizing is often considered to be more dangerous than de-energizing. Before re-energizing, you must:

- notify personnel to stay clear

Fig. 3-1. Tags indicate work in progress

- inspect the area to make certain that all tools and supplies have been removed

- secure enclosure doors

- remove locks and tags.

Electrical Safety Lockout

3.04   If the unexpected start-up of equipment is likely to endanger you or other people, you cannot simply de-energize the equipment. The switch you turn off might be turned on again by someone else. Power to the equipment must be locked out at the main disconnect before work begins. A padlock and a multiple-lock hasp, with instructions for their use, should be available to every electrical worker in the plant. Sometimes you might need more than one lock to lock out every power source supplying the electrical equipment to be serviced.

3.05   Most switch boxes are made so that a padlock can be snapped into place. Before you work on a machine, lock out the main power source and leave the padlock in place until you finish the job, or until you are relieved by another worker who will replace your lock with his or her own.

3.06   Even when the power is locked out, wear protective equipment and use insulated tools. To prevent accidents, treat dead circuits as though they are live. Test any circuit before starting work to make sure it is de-energized. This precaution can prevent an accident.

OSHA Lockout/Tagout Procedures

3.07   OSHA has established standards covering lockout and tagout (29 CFR 1910.147 and 1910.333). They are designed to help safeguard workers from hazardous energy while they are performing maintenance on machines or equipment. The standards state that equipment must be turned off and disconnected from the energy source prior to servicing. In addition, they require employers to develop written lockout/tagout procedures, to train all those employees who could be injured by accidental start-up or the release of stored energy, and to carry out periodic inspections (at least annually) to ensure that the energy control procedures are being implemented properly.

3.08   The OSHA standards include guidelines for bringing about a zero energy state, which makes it impossible for a machine to be activated accidentally while someone is working on it. You should never work on a machine until you have brought it to this state.

3.09   Lockout/tagout. Bringing machinery to a zero energy state begins with locking out the power. Each worker should have an assigned lock, a key, and a lockout device. No two keys should fit the same lock. Your initials or your clock number should be stamped on your lock. The procedure for locking out the power to a piece of equipment consists of the following steps:

- Notify the operator that you will be working on the machine.

- Turn off the electric power and attach the lockout device to the energy-isolating device (that is, the circuit breaker or disconnect switch) in such a way that the power cannot be turned on.

- Place your own padlock on the lockout device. Anyone else who is working on the same equipment should add his or her own lock to the lockout device.

- Place an appropriate warning sign (tag) at the controls indicating that work is in progress. An example is shown in Fig. 3-1.

3.10   In order to bring a machine to a zero energy state, you must take the following steps after you have locked out the power and before you begin work:

- Push the START button to make sure that the power is disconnected. Then push the STOP button (to prevent accidental start-up once power is turned on again).

- Make sure that all moving parts of the equipment have come to a complete stop.

- Check for pneumatic and hydraulic lines in the machinery. (They should be marked with labels or signs.) If they affect the area in which you are going to work, bleed, drain, or purge them to eliminate the pressure. Vent air valves to the atmosphere and drain surge tanks and reservoirs to prevent pressure buildup in the lines. The valves controlling these lines should then be locked out. A lockout device on a valve is shown in Fig. 3-2.

Fig. 3-2. Valve lockout device

- Now check for mechanisms that are under spring tension or compression or are suspended. Block, clamp, or chain them in position.

- Check for sharp or projecting parts or surfaces that can cut or gouge you. Either remove them or pad them, whichever is easier.

- Make a voltage measurement at the point of exposure.

3.11   When you have completed your work, inspect the work area to make sure that all tools and other items have been cleaned up and that all safety guards are in place. Other workers should stand a safe distance from equipment or circuits being re-energized. Do not turn on electricity, compressed air, or water, and never start any machinery without first checking to make sure no one is in a position to be injured.

3.12   When the inspection is complete, remove your own lock. The last worker to remove his or her lock also may remove the lockout device. Never remove anyone else's lock or tag, and never allow anyone to remove yours. If you lose your key, notify your supervisor at once and get a new lock and key. Finally, test the machinery for proper operation and notify the operator that the machine is back in operating condition.

3.13   **Tagout.** In most cases, warning tags are used along with locks. In some cases, however, lockout might not be possible. Equipment must then be tagged out. Lockout is the preferred method, since no one can remove your lock without your key. Tags are not as safe as locks, because they can easily be removed, overlooked, or ignored. In tagout applications, it becomes even more important for all employees to receive the proper training. Everyone must be aware of correct tagout procedures to ensure safe working conditions.

3.14   Essentially, a tag or tagout device is a warning device that takes the place of a lock without providing the physical restraint of a lock. A tag simply identifies a source of potential danger and indicates that the equipment being worked on may not be operated until the tag is removed. Tags should never be bypassed or ignored.

3.15   For an electrical tagout, OSHA requires that you disconnect the circuit in another location. Methods include pulling a fuse or opening a disconnect.

3.16   Keep in mind that lockout/tagout procedures are not for the purpose of slowing you down or making your job more difficult—they are for your safety. But you must do more than follow the rules. For example, if your plant does not have enough lockout devices available, ask for them. Even if you feel that a project will take only a few minutes to complete, use the lockout system.

3.17   Never put up with someone else's failure to follow the energy control procedures established in your plant. If the procedures are being bypassed or if part of the procedure is lacking, report the situation to your supervisor or someone else who can correct the problem. Remember that you can be injured by someone else's failure to follow safe working procedures.

3.18   Your only sure protection is to bring each machine you work on to a zero energy state. Workers who have not learned this chapter are the ones who suffer the most serious injuries. Take no chances. Take no shortcuts. Do not depend on someone else to protect you from danger in the plant. Take those few extra moments to do the job right and protect yourself.

Using Power Tools Safely

3.19   One of your most frequent encounters with electrical equipment will probably be with portable power tools. The main electrical danger when using power tools is the short circuit. Metal parts of any tool, machine, or structure can become current conductors if damage occurs to electrical wiring or insulation.

3.20   When a short circuit occurs, the handle or case of the tool becomes part of the circuit. Remember, electricity takes any available path to the ground. If the tool has not been grounded properly, one path to the ground is through the body of the worker holding the tool. The result might be only a mild shock. But it might be a serious burn or a fatal jolt of electricity.

3.21   When using power tools, your body is protected by the grounding wire, which provides a low-resistance path from metal to ground and carries away most of the current. However, this path never carries all the current. If your body is not insulated from the ground and comes in contact with the circuit, you will receive a shock. When correctly designed and connected, the low-resistance path should make the shock harmless. In places where high ground conductivity creates a lower-than-normal resistance through the worker, a ground fault circuit interrupter (GFCI) should be used. These devices are covered in detail in the following chapter.

3.22   Stationary electrical equipment can be grounded permanently by connecting all metal parts through a heavy conductor to a metal water

Fig. 3-3. Three-wire plug and receptacle

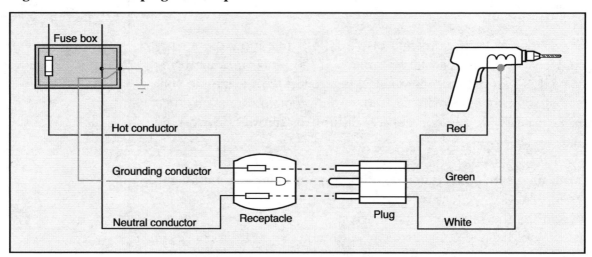

pipe or other metal structure buried in the ground. Both the connection and the structure should be checked frequently to ensure that their resistance remains low. If plastic fittings and pipes are used to carry water, another ground must be selected in order to provide an uninterrupted metallic path to ground. Otherwise, the equipment will not be grounded. Equipment grounding will be covered in more detail in Chapter Five.

3.23   Electrically powered portable tools and other portable equipment require a more involved procedure to ground them and make them safe. Most portable power tools have three wires in the line cord and come equipped with three-prong plugs, as shown in Fig. 3-3. The third wire is a grounding wire connected to the metal housing of the tool. If there is a short circuit to the housing of the tool, this wire carries the current to ground. The fuse blows, but the worker feels little or nothing. You can see how this arrangement works by comparing Fig. 3-4A and Fig. 3-4B. When using these tools, it is necessary only to provide three-slot receptacles that are reliably grounded.

3.24   Unfortunately, the three-prong grounding system has two drawbacks. The most serious one is that the system is easily bypassed. If a grounded receptacle is not available, do not be tempted to use a two-prong adapter. This adapter—commonly called a "suicide plug"—is not considered a reliable method of grounding. Another way to bypass the system is to break off the grounding pin on the plug, thereby breaking the grounding path. Even if you use a three-prong plug, there is no guarantee that the receptacle is connected to a reliable ground.

3.25   The second drawback occurs if the tool is properly grounded and you touch an ungrounded, faulted electrical device—for example, a live wire with faulty insulation. In this case, fault current passes through your body.

Fig. 3-4. Grounding wire carries current to ground

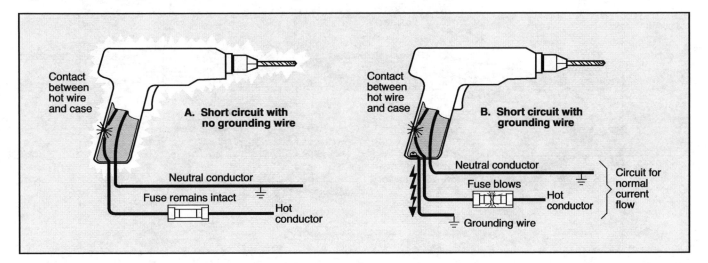

3.26 Most power tools made today are equipped with three-conductor cords and polarized grounding plugs. Some tools, however, are double-insulated and do not require grounding. These two-wire tools are sometimes used in place of three-wire grounded equipment. They are the only two-wire tools that can be used safely. Use these tools whenever possible. They should be plainly labeled to indicate that they are double-insulated.

3.27 The ordinary insulation of wires is called *functional insulation*. All electric tools have this insulation, as it is necessary to direct the current for the proper functioning of the tool. In the tool shown in Fig. 3-5, functional insulation is used around all current-carrying components—brushes, armature windings, stator coils, commutator, and wiring.

Fig. 3-5. Power tool with functional insulation

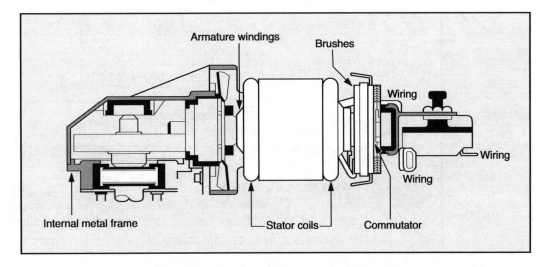

Fig. 3-6. Double-insulated tool

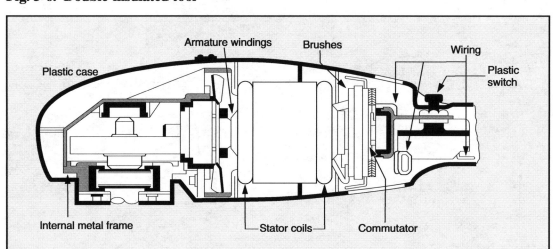

3.28 Double-insulated tools have an additional, independent insulation system called *protective insulation*. The extra insulation protects the operator against electric shock if the functional insulation fails. The double-insulated tool in Fig. 3-6 has an armature construction similar to that of a conventional tool. The motor assembly is mounted in a metal skeleton frame that is housed in a plastic, non-conducting case. The housing of the switch is also plastic. If a metal case is used, it has a plastic liner that isolates any metal parts that might become energized if the functional insulation fails. In addition, the tool shaft or arbor is fitted with an insulating sleeve. Double-insulated tools must be kept clean and dry. If you use them, handle them carefully so the insulation is not damaged and always inspect them before use.

3.29 Misuse of a tool by an operator is a major cause of insulation breakdown. Another cause is the entry of metal chips or other foreign particles and contaminants into the tool. These particles often enter through the tool's cooling system.

Power Tool Safety Rules

3.30 When you use electric power tools, follow these safety rules to reduce your chances of being injured.

- Understand the intended uses and limitations of the tool before beginning to work with it. Know the potential hazards involved.

- Always use a GFCI when working with a three-wire grounded tool.

- Inspect all power tools before use, including all guards, the case, the line cord, and accessories. Never, under any circumstances, use a damaged or faulty power tool. Never use a tool with a frayed or cracked power cord. When electric-powered tools are in need of repair, apply a lockout device and danger tag on the plug end to guard against accidental use. Turn in the tool for repair, or repair it yourself if you are authorized to do so. Maintaining power tools keeps them efficient as well as safe.

- Do not cut or drill into any surface until you have made sure that there are no electric wires that you might cut into or scrape. If you cut into a concealed wire, a short circuit might result. Make sure that any electrical power lines you are working on or near are turned off. Many accidents result from cutting into power lines. Route electrical cords so that they will not be cut or tripped over.

- Do not operate an electric tool on a wet surface, and do not set it down on one. A wet surface increases the possibility and the severity of an electric shock.

- Make particularly sure that all the circuits are in safe operating condition before you use the tool. Remember that the tool will work even if the equipment grounding wire is disconnected, broken, or bypassed. That third wire is the one that protects you from shock and burns.

- Whenever you change bits, blades, or other accessories, make sure that you have first turned off the power and pulled the plug. Turn off tools when you finish a job or temporarily stop working. The next user of a tool might start it accidentally when reconnecting it if it is left on. As an added precaution, make sure the switch is off before plugging in a tool. Never leave a running tool unattended.

- Many electric tools have a safety feature called a "deadman" trigger or switch. This switch automatically cuts off the power when the pressure of the operator's hand or finger is removed. Never try to bypass this feature by wiring or taping the switch in position.

Recognizing Electric Shock Victims

3.31   Sometimes, despite all your precautions, an accident might occur. If that accident involves electric shock, some specialized procedures might be required to save the victim's life.

3.32   Often it is not easy to recognize the symptoms of electric shock. A victim might or might not have any external symptoms However, some clues are:

- loss of consciousness

- irregular or weak pulse

- difficulty breathing

- burns at the entry and exit points of the current.

3.33   All shock victims or suspected victims should receive prompt medical attention, even if they appear to be uninjured or claim to feel fine. Some internal injuries will not be obvious to the untrained observer. These injuries can, however, cause extreme pain. Sometimes breathing and circulatory problems can develop hours after contact. For this reason, any shock victim should be observed by a medical professional.

First Aid for Shock Victims

3.34   The most important things to know about first aid for shock victims are:

- Never touch a shock victim who is still in contact with the electrical source.

- Act quickly—seconds count! Your actions could make the difference between life and death.

- Do not offer first aid unless you are qualified. You could make things worse.

- Get medical assistance as soon as possible for any victim of electric shock. First aid is essential, but professional medical attention might be necessary, even if the victim appears to have recovered.

3.35   If you touch someone who is in contact with the electrical source, you too will become part of the circuit. Then there will be two victims instead of one. Although it is important to act quickly, it is even more important to think before you act!

3.36   A victim who contacts a live conductor might be thrown free as a result of muscle spasms. If, however, the person is "frozen" to the energized conductor, the first thing to do is to shut off the electricity. If the shutoff is very far away, drag or push the victim away from the electricity with a piece of nonconductive material. Make sure that the material you use is dry. Using moist or damp material to disconnect the victim from an energized circuit is a much greater hazard. If live wires are lying on or near the victim, use a nonconductive material to move them away.

3.37   Start first aid as soon as it is safe to do so. Move the victim only if he is in an unsafe location. Unnecessary movement could make a spinal injury worse if one is present. Treat burns with cool compresses or immerse the burned area in cool water.

3.38   If the victim is conscious, call for professional assistance. Then question him about what happened. This information could be important to medical professionals. Stay with the victim until help arrives.

3.39   If the victim is unconscious, call for medical assistance, then check for breathing and a pulse. If the victim seems to be breathing regularly, keep him warm and stay with him until help arrives. Do not try to give him anything to drink if he is unconscious. If there is no breathing or pulse, you must act within approximately 4 minutes or the victim is likely to suffer permanent brain damage. After 6 minutes without a pulse or respiration, brain damage or death almost always occurs.

3.40   All workers, especially those who work with electricity, should be trained in cardiopulmonary resuscitation (CPR). CPR is an emergency procedure used to restore respiration and blood circulation after these functions have stopped. It makes it possible to revive a person from what would otherwise have been a fatal electric shock. Once a person's heartbeat and breathing have stopped, that person is considered clinically dead. Permanent damage from a lack of oxygen occurs first in the brain, then in other organs of the body. The sooner CPR is begun (see Fig. 3-7), the less chance there is for brain damage.

Fig. 3-7. Cardiac compression to restore circulation

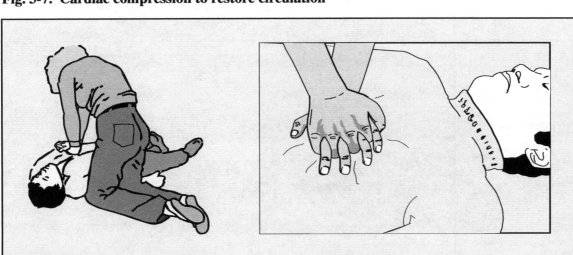

3.41   Prompt and proper application of CPR can also save the life of someone who would otherwise die as a result of heart attack, drowning, suffocation, choking, or automobile accident. If you are not trained in CPR or need a refresher course, check with your plant safety department, your local fire or police department, the American Red Cross, or the American Heart Association.

Chapter Four

The *National Electrical Code*®

Overview of the *NEC*

4.01   The official document name for the *National Electrical Code (NEC)* is NFPA 70. The National Fire Protection Association publishes a new edition of the *NEC* every three years. During the period between editions, several *NEC* committees gather information and suggested amendments that have been submitted. The amendments and revisions are reviewed, and the agreed-upon changes are made to improve the *NEC*. The *NEC* articles are nationally used as the standard for electrical installations. In addition to the *NEC*, many states have adopted state-mandated electrical requirements as well.

4.02   Before you begin to use and attempt to interpret the *NEC*, it is important to understand how the document is organized. The *National Electrical Code* contains useful and important information, but locating that information can be difficult and time consuming. Once you develop a better understanding of how the *NEC* is laid out, you will find it to be much more user-friendly and effective.

4.03   The *NEC* begins with an introduction, which explains the purpose and scope of the document and gives other general information. The introduction is followed by nine chapters:

- Chapters 1, 2, 3, and 4 apply generally. They cover definitions and installation information (voltages, markings, connections, etc.), circuits and circuit protection, wiring and cables, and general-purpose equipment such as switches, cords, and receptacles. These four chapters are the ones that are the most commonly referenced.

- Chapters 5, 6, and 7 apply to special occupancies, special equipment, and special conditions.

- Chapter 8 applies to communications systems.

- Chapter 9 contains tables and examples.

Chapter 9 is followed by several annexes. These annexes include referenced standards, calculations, and additional tables and examples that help implement the code requirements.

4.04   Each chapter contains a number of articles. The first digit of each article number corresponds to the chapter number. For example, Article 240.6 can be found in Chapter 2 and Article 404.2 can be found in Chapter 4. The *NEC* also contains a variety of tables that are numbered much like the articles. For example, you can tell that Table 310.15(B)(16) is found in Chapter 3 because the number begins with a 3. An index is included to help locate topics throughout the *NEC*.

4.05   Although using the *National Electrical Code* can be difficult at times, there are some things you can do to help optimize its potential. The first tip is to use tabs for each article or group of articles to allow you to turn to a particular topic quickly. These tabs can save a lot of time and eliminate some of the confusion involved in locating articles or tables. A second tip is to use different colored highlighters to mark key references. It is easy to get lost in all the wording of the *NEC*, and highlighting is a good way to identify commonly used articles.

4.06   When you first look at the *NEC* book, you will notice that some text has gray shading. The *NEC Handbook* contains some tan-shaded text. This shading indicates that a change has been made from the previous edition. This is a valuable tool for quickly identifying revisions that have occurred. In addition, you will see vertical rules in the left margin of the code book, next to some text. These rules indicate new material that was added in the current edition. Bullets (•) in the text column indicate that some information was removed.

4.07   Informational Notes are another feature of the *NEC*. These notes were previously called Fine Print Notes or FPNs. They are often used to provide additional information about certain articles or tables. Notes located at the bottom of tables can include information concerning alternative calculations, such as the notes found on Table 220.55. Informational Notes not only provide additional information, but they can direct you to examples or other sources of reference.

4.08   Exceptions are another important element of the *NEC* articles. Exceptions are situations that deviate from the stated rule or code reference. An example can be found in Table 310.15(B)(2)(a). This particular table has multiple exceptions that are allowed. Some *NEC* references must allow for exceptions in order to maintain safety and functionality. Always check for exceptions to any reference.

4.09   Article 90 of the *NEC* contains introductory material that defines the purpose, scope, and format of the document. It lays the foundation for how the *NEC* is arranged and how it is enforced. The first section, Article 90.1, states the purpose of the *NEC* as "the practical safeguarding of persons and property from hazards arising from the use of electricity." Article 90.3 describes how the *NEC* is arranged and is a good reference for understanding the layout of the chapters.

4.10   The scope of the *NEC* is important to understand when installing electrical systems. Article 90.2(A) outlines which installations are covered in the *NEC* and which are not. For example, some installations covered by the *NEC* are as follows:

- public and private premises (see Fig. 4-1)

- yards, lots, carnivals, and industrial substations

- conductors and equipment connected to supply voltage

- installations used in electrical utility structures that are not an integral part of a generating plant, utility substation, or control center.

4.11   Article 90.2(B) lists several installations not covered by the *NEC* (see Fig. 4-2 on the following page):

Fig. 4-1. Typical structures covered by the *NEC*

Fig. 4-2. Aircraft, railroad, and watercraft installations are not covered

- ships, watercraft, and aircraft

- mines and mining machinery

- railroads and railway systems

- communications equipment under the exclusive control of communications utilities

- installations under the exclusive control of electric utilities.

Chapter 1: General *NEC*

4.12   Article 100 contains many terms and definitions used within the *NEC*. Not every term used in the code is listed in Article 100, usually only those used in two or more articles. Article 100 attempts to provide definitions of terms that are vital to proper application of the *NEC*, not terms that are generally defined in a common dictionary. Article 100 is intended to assist you and other workers in reducing misunderstanding and improving communication. For example, "continuous load" is defined as a load that is expected to continue for at least three hours. An article referenced in a later chapter of the *NEC* might contain the term "continuous load" but not offer an explanation. Article 100 provides the specific definition essential for proper code application. You should be aware that many *NEC* articles also have definitions specific to that article at the start of the article. These definitions are always listed with the form "xxx.2 Definitions." Some examples are 310.2, 480.2, and 552.2.

4.13   Article 110 covers some general information on requirements for electrical installations. For example, a general installation requirement is found in Article 110.12(A). This article addresses the unused openings commonly found in electrical enclosures, as shown in Fig. 4-3. All unused openings must be effectively closed according to Article 110.12(A).

4.14   Other commonly used references in Article 110 concern working space requirements and guarding from live parts. Article 110 features Table 110.26(A)(1) and Table 110.34(A), which provide information concerning working space requirements around live parts. These requirements are in place to avoid accidental contact with live electrical conductors or energized parts.

4.15   The following are some key *NEC* references from Chapter 1:

- **110.12(A)** Unused Openings

- **110.14(C)** Temperature Limitations

- **110.15** High-Leg Marking

- **110.26** Spaces About Electrical Equipment.

Fig. 4-3. Unused openings

Chapter 2: Wiring and Protection

4.16   Articles 200 through 285 make up a commonly used part of the *NEC*. Electricians spend a great deal of time referencing this chapter in the field. It covers branch circuits, services, overcurrent protection, grounding and bonding, and several other topics. You can also find information on the spacing of outlets, branch circuit ratings, feeder and service sizing, and service calculations.

4.17   Article 210 is an important part of Chapter 2. It provides information concerning branch circuits. For example, Article 210 describes where receptacle outlets should be located and mandates the minimum number of branch circuits required. Branch circuit ratings are also referenced in this article. Another important part of Article 210 relates to ground fault circuit interrupter receptacles (GFCIs). Article 210.8(A) lists the required locations of GFCI receptacles in dwelling units:

- bathrooms

Fig. 4-4. GFCI receptacle

- garages

- outdoors

- crawl spaces

- unfinished basements.

Figure 4-4 shows a GFCI receptacle, as referenced in Article 210.8(A).

4.18   Article 220 provides information about branch circuit, feeder, and service calculations. Anyone who works with electricity should be very familiar with this article. Within it, you will find vital information on how to calculate electrical lighting, appliance, HVAC, and other loads properly. Numerous tables are used to determine load demand factors, including Table 220.12, Table 220.42, Table 220.54, and Table 220.55.

4.19   An electrician will also use Article 220 to determine the proper electrical load for residential and commercial installations. This article should be consulted before performing electrical installations for branch circuits, feeders, and electrical services. Improper calculations can result in overloads and/or other hazardous conditions. A standard method of calculation is provided in Article 220, along with other optional methods. The method that best meets local building codes and requirements should be used before installations are performed.

4.20   Electrical service installations are the topic of Article 230. There are specific requirements related to sizing, supporting, and clearances of overhead service conductors. Article 230 outlines how to safely and effectively install both overhead and underground electrical services that bring power into a structure.

4.21   Overcurrent protection is a very important element of electrical installations. Article 240 addresses the requirements for installing fuses, circuit breakers, and other overcurrent protection devices. In this article of the *NEC*, you will find the calculation and installation requirements for each of these types of devices. Figure 4-5 shows an example of some common overcurrent protection devices.

4.22   Article 250 contains information about grounding and bonding procedures. Proper grounding and bonding practices can mean the difference between life and death. Anyone who works with electricity should have a thorough understanding of Article 250. This article describes grounding connections, electrodes, equipment grounding conductors, and other grounding topics.

4.23   The following are some key *NEC* references from Chapter 2:

- **210.8** Ground Fault Circuit Interrupter Protection for Personnel

- **210.52** Dwelling Unit Receptacle Outlets

- **220.14** Other Loads—All Occupancies

- **220.40–220.61** Feeder and Service Load Calculations

- **240.4** Protection of Conductors

- **240.6(A)** Fuses and Fixed-Trip Circuit Breakers

- **250.50–250.70** Grounding Electrode System and Grounding Electrode Conductor.

Chapter 3: Wiring Methods and Materials

4.24   Articles 300 through 399 are also commonly referenced by electrical workers because of the scope of the material they contain. Information in these articles relates to wiring installation, burial requirements, conductor ampacity, and box-fill calculations, as well as different types of cables and conduit. Several tables are used to perform calculations for a variety of installations.

Fig. 4-5. Fuses and circuit breakers

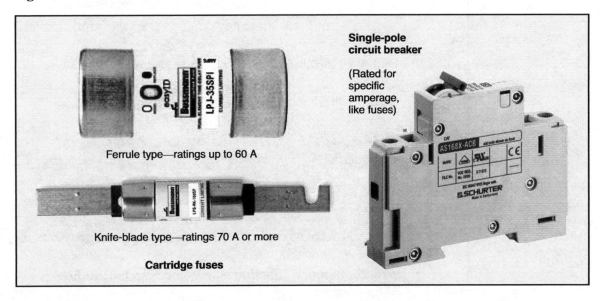

Single-pole circuit breaker

(Rated for specific amperage, like fuses)

Ferrule type—ratings up to 60 A

Knife-blade type—ratings 70 A or more

Cartridge fuses

48

Fig. 4-6. Box-fill calculations are covered in Article 314.16

4.25 Article 310 addresses conductors for general wiring. One of the most commonly used tables in the *NEC*, which gives the allowable ampacity of conductors, is Table 310.15(B)(16). This article also contains information about adjustment factors for current-carrying conductors.

4.26 Articles 312 through 314 provide important information concerning the installation of cabinets, boxes, and enclosures. Article 314 also contains an important reference in Table 314.16(A), which determines the allowable box fill. Box-fill calculations are important, because overcrowding an enclosure with conductors can result in overheating and fire hazards. Figure 4-6 shows a typical metal box with several conductors. A calculation should be performed to ensure that the number of conductors in the box does not exceed the available space. Table 314.16(A) can be used to help determine the required space.

4.27 Articles 320 through 340 provide requirements for various types of cables. Each of these articles lists the uses permitted and the uses not permitted for the individual cable type. Their insulation is also described and support specifications included.

4.28 Articles 342 through 392 address the different types of conduit and other protective enclosures for running wire used in the electrical industry. Each article lists the specific requirements for the each conduit, including its intended uses, maximum number of bends, and support specifications. Information about busways, wire gutters, and cable trays can also be found in this section of the *NEC*.

4.29 The following are some key *NEC* references from Chapter 3:

- **300.4** Protection Against Physical Damage

- **Table 300.5** Minimum Cover Requirements

- **Table 310.15(B)(16)** Allowable Ampacities of Insulated Conductors

- **Table 314.16(A)** Metal Boxes

- **Table 314.16(B)** Volume Allowance Required per Conductor

- **314.28** Pull and Junction Boxes and Conduit Bodies.

Chapter 4: Equipment for General Use

4.30   Chapter 4 of the *NEC* covers an assortment of general-purpose equipment in Articles 400 through 490. Some of the equipment addressed includes switches, panelboards, luminaires, appliances, motors, and transformers. Chapter 4 concludes the general-use portion of the *NEC*.

4.31   Chapter 4 begins with Articles 400 and 402, which discuss flexible cords and fixture wires. Several charts and tables are included in these articles to provide information about voltage, insulation, and cable usage. The temperature ratings of various cable and fixture wires are also provided in these articles.

4.32   Articles 404 through 409 cover switches, receptacles, and panelboards. Information can be found concerning switch connections and installations. Other information includes the procedure for replacing non-grounding type receptacles and panelboard wiring. Figure 4-7 shows examples of panelboards.

4.33   Articles 410 and 411 relate to the installation of luminaires and low-voltage lighting systems. This section is especially important because it describes how to install lighting safely to reduce the risk of fire. Luminaires must be installed according to specifications related to location and clearance.

4.34   Articles 422 through 427 apply to appliances and heating equipment. Appliance wiring covered in this section can include items such as garbage disposals, central vacuum systems, ranges, and water

Fig. 4-7. Electrical distribution panels

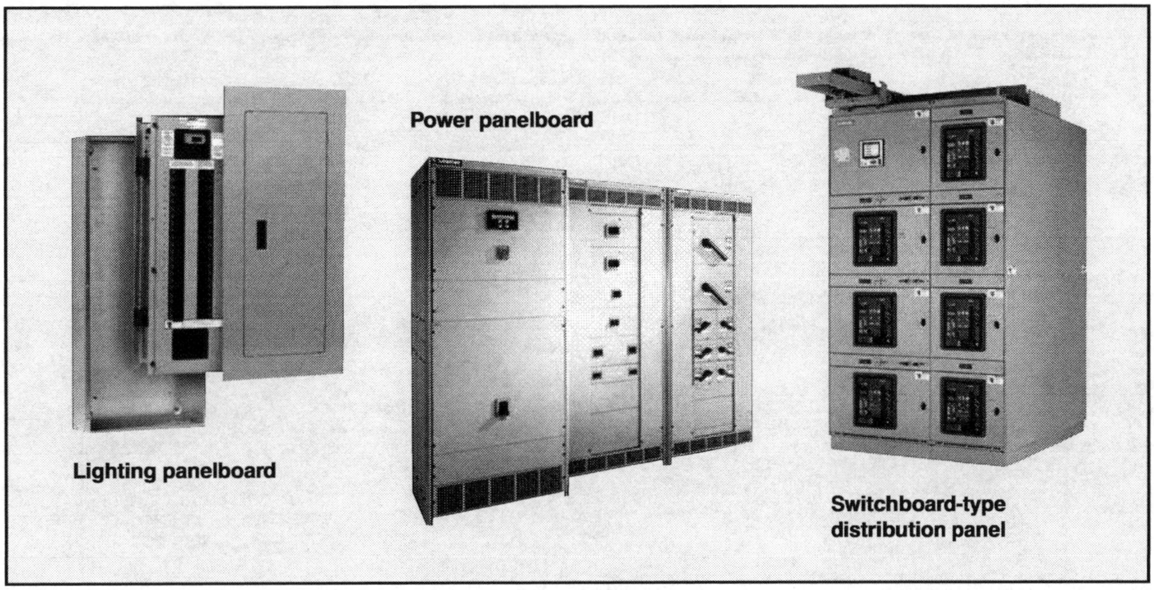

Power panelboard

Lighting panelboard

Switchboard-type distribution panel

heaters. Fixed heating equipment is also found in this section. Most of the articles concerning heating equipment are related to installing the equipment according to manufacturer's specifications and in accordance with safety regulations.

4.35   Article 430 is the most widely used section of Chapter 4. It deals with single- and three-phase motors, motor circuits, and controllers. Article 430 spells out the steps necessary to determine full-load current, overload protection, conductor sizing, and other important motor installation requirements. Motor calculations should be performed based upon the *NEC* requirements to ensure proper motor and motor circuit protection. Figure 4-8 shows a motor circuit calculation diagram. It shows how various *NEC* articles relate to each part of the calculation.

4.36   Chapter 4 concludes with Articles 440 through 490. These articles discuss air-conditioning equipment, generators, transformers, and batteries. In this section, you can locate the disconnecting means requirements for equipment, overcurrent protection ratings, and grounding specifications for each of these. Article 490 addresses the requirements for equipment that is rated over 600 V.

4.37   The following are some key *NEC* references from Chapter 4:

- **400.6(A)** Standard (Flexible Cable and Cord) Markings

- **404.14** Rating and Use of Snap Switches

- **406.4** General Installation Requirements (Receptacles)

- **410.10** Luminaires in Specific Locations

Fig. 4-8. Motor circuit calculations

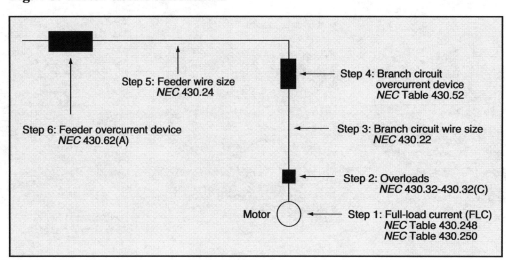

- **Table 430.248** Full-Load Currents, Single-Phase Alternating-Current Motors

- **Table 430.250** Full-Load Current, Three-Phase Alternating-Current Motors.

Chapter 5: Special Occupancies

4.38   Chapter 5 of the *NEC* defines the requirements for special occupancies and locations. Such occupancies include hazardous locations, commercial garages, and healthcare facilities. Chapter 5 begins the second portion of the *NEC* and may not be as commonly used as the previous four chapters. However, the contents of Chapter 5 and the remaining chapters of the *NEC* are still very important because of their specific requirements. They are intended to modify or supplement the first four chapters.

4.39   Articles 500 through 510 are associated with hazardous locations. Hazardous locations are divided into three classes and then subdivided within each class. Class I locations include areas where flammable gases, vapors, and liquids are present. Class II locations are areas that contain combustible dusts. In Class III locations, combustible fibers are present.

4.40   Articles 511 through 590 provide details on various special locations. Some of these special locations include spray booths, mobile homes, marinas, and temporary-wiring installations. Article 514 contains electrical installation requirements for fuel-dispensing facilities like the one shown in Figure 4-9. The tables and figures in the article convey how the areas around fueling stations are classified by class, division, and zone.

4.41   Healthcare facilities are covered in Article 517. Special electrical installation requirements are necessary for medical equipment. Ground-fault protection and alternative power sources are of great concern when dealing with medical equipment. Emergency system power is critical to life support machines and other vital medical equipment.

4.42   Manufactured home and mobile home requirements are found in Article 550. Electrical installations in these types of homes vary from the previous residential articles of Chapter 2.

Fig. 4-9. Fuel-dispensing station

Manufactured homes and mobile homes require different service calculations than those used for typical permanent residential homes.

4.43   The following are some key *NEC* references from Chapter 5:

- **500.5** Classifications of (Hazardous) Locations

- **Table 514.3(B)(1)** Class I Locations—Motor Fuel Dispensing Facilities

- **517.2** Definitions (Health Care Facilities)

- **550.12** Branch Circuits (Manufactured Homes, Mobile Homes).

Chapter 6: Special Equipment

4.44   Chapter 6 covers the use and installation of special equipment. The rules set forth in this chapter supplement or modify the general rules that may exist in previous *NEC* chapters. Chapter 6 is of particular interest to those working as specialists on the equipment contained in the articles of this chapter.

4.45   Article 600 deals with the installation of electric signs and outline lighting. This is perhaps the most widely used portion of Chapter 6, because most commercial buildings use lighted signs and/or neon lighting. Article 600 discusses branch circuit requirements, grounding, and ballasts in relation to electric signs and lighting. Figure 4-10 shows a typical electric sign that must meet the requirements associated with Article 600.

Fig. 4-10. Electric sign

4.46   Article 680 is another commonly used portion of Chapter 6. It covers swimming pools, fountains, and other similar installations. Obviously, electricity and water are a dangerous combination, so an electrical worker must go to great lengths to ensure proper grounding and bonding are established. In Article 680, the *NEC* addresses the specific rules for the installation of underwater lighting fixtures, conductors, junction boxes, and grounding.

4.47   There are many other types of special equipment addressed in Chapter 6. Some of the most common include cranes and hoists, elevators, welding machines, x-ray equipment, electrolytic cells, and fire pumps. Article 690, covering solar photovoltaic systems, was expanded in the latest edition of the *NEC* due to their rapidly increasing use in industry.

4.48   The following are some key *NEC* references from Chapter 6:

- **600.7** Grounding and Bonding (Electric Signs and Outline Lighting)

- **630.11–630.15** Arc Welders

- **630.31–630.34** Resistance Welders

- **Table 680.8** Overhead Conductor Clearances (Swimming Pools, Fountains).

Chapter 7: Special Conditions

4.49   Chapter 7 of the *NEC* addresses the need for wiring methods and rules that apply to special conditions. Special conditions exist when there is a deviation from the normal, general application of the *NEC* standards. This chapter explores such special conditions as emergency systems, standby systems, and remote-control circuits.

4.50   Articles 700 through 702 apply to emergency systems and standby systems. Emergency systems are required to supply illumination and power in the event that the normal electrical supply is interrupted. Figure 4-11 shows a common emergency lighting unit that would be activated in the event of a power failure. Standby systems serve as alternative power supplies for critical circuits in the event of a power failure.

4.51   Another important part of Chapter 7 is Article 725, which covers signal circuits. A typical example of a signal circuit is the security alarm system that might be found in a home or business. Intercom systems, like those found in schools or hospitals, are also signal circuits. These circuits are typically operated at less than 30 V.

4.52   Article 760 relates to fire alarm systems, which are considered another special condition. Although fire alarms systems generally operate at less than 30 V and are considered signaling

Fig. 4-11. Emergency light

circuits, they require different rules for installation because of their critical nature. The circuits described in Article 760 are controlled only by a fire alarm system. The circuits described in Article 725 are controlled by other systems in the building.

4.53   The following are some key *NEC* references from Chapter 7:

- **700.10** Wiring, Emergency System

- **700.12** Sources of Power (Emergency Systems)

- **700.15** Loads on Emergency Branch Circuits

- **725.2** Definitions (Remote-Control, Signaling, Power-Limited Circuits).

Chapter 8: Communications Systems

4.54   Chapter 8 is made up of Articles 800 through 840, which relate to communications systems. These systems can include telephone, radio, television, and telegraph installations, as well as cable systems that are not controlled by utility companies. Outside wiring for alarm systems is also covered.

4.55   One of the main concerns when working with communication circuits is maintaining adequate separation from electrical power conductors. Proper grounding is an important topic in Article 800. Figure 4-12 shows communication system wiring that must meet the requirements associated with Article 800.

Fig. 4-12. Communication system wiring

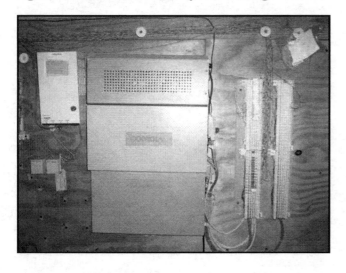

4.56   Articles 810 through 840 deal with radio and television equipment, including amateur radio and citizen band equipment, and vertical rod and dish antennas. These articles also include information about community antenna television and broadband communications systems. Broadband systems include voice, audio, video, and data systems.

4.57   The following are some key *NEC* references from Chapter 8:

- **Table 800.154(a)** Applications of Listed Communications Wires, Cables, and Raceways

- **Table 800.179** Cable Markings

- **Table 820.154(a)** Applications of Listed Coaxial Cables in Buildings.

Chapter 9: Tables

4.58   Chapter 9 consists of 12 tables. These tables support referenced sections of the *NEC*. For example, Article 344 is also referenced in Table 4 of Chapter 9.

4.59   Tables 1 and 4 are used when performing conduit-fill calculations. An electrician would use these tables to calculate the allowable percent fill in the various types of conduit. For example, Article 358 contains information about electrical metallic tubing. Table 4 contains helpful information related to Article 358 by providing the dimensions and percent area of the conduit. Instead of listing this information in Article 358, the *NEC* combined all of this information for each type of conduit into Table 4 for easier reference.

4.60   Table 5 is also commonly used in conduit-fill calculations. This table lists the dimensions of insulated conductors and fixture wires. Table 5 is typically useful in conjunction with Table 4 when the individual dimension of a conductor is needed in the calculation.

4.61   Table 8 provides the conductor properties for every conductor size ranging from 18 AWG to 2000 kcmil. The information found in this table includes the diameter, area, and resistance for each conductor. Table 8 is commonly used for voltage-drop calculations.

Annexes

4.62   The annexes located after Chapter 9 are not NFPA requirements, but are included for informational purposes only. They simply provide additional and helpful support of the *NEC* articles. When attempting to interpret the *NEC*, it is always beneficial to have additional information to assist you in understanding the articles.

4.63   Two of the most widely used annexes are Annex C and Annex D. Annex C provides information about conduit fill. This annex is made up of numerous tables for each individual type of conduit. An electrician could use Annex C to determine the maximum number of conductors allowed in a particular conduit. Users of Annex C should note that there are two sets of tables. One set is for standard conductors and the other, marked (A), is for compact conductors. Annex D provides examples of a variety of calculations addressed throughout the articles of the *NEC*.

Chapter Five

Grounding, Ground Faults, and Short Circuits

Equipment Grounding

5.01   A *ground* is any connection between an electric circuit and the earth. Proper grounding helps equipment users avoid contact with hot circuits and also helps limit voltages when one circuit shorts to an adjacent circuit. Unplanned connections to ground are called *ground faults* or *unintentional grounds*. Ground faults generally occur when equipment insulation has been damaged. They also can occur when equipment is abused—when, for example, an electric power tool is accidentally placed in water.

5.02   Electrical equipment is grounded with a separate, green or green-and-yellow striped wire. The grounding wire carries current only when a ground fault occurs between the hot conductor and the housing of the equipment or tool. If the fault current is large enough, it will blow the fuse or trip the circuit breaker. If not, most of the fault current will flow through the grounding wire. Keep in mind, however, that some current can still pass through your body. Ungrounded two-wire equipment provides no protection. If the housing becomes energized, the electricity can only flow to ground through your body.

5.03   If two-slot receptacles are in service, they should be replaced with properly wired three-slot receptacles before using any piece of equipment that has a three-prong plug. Notice in Fig. 5-1, on the following page, that the shape and arrangement of the prongs and the slots make it impossible to connect the grounding wire incorrectly. This arrangement does not mean that protective measures will always work well, however.

5.04   If the grounding wire is not connected properly or securely or if the grounding system is in poor condition, it will not be effective. This situation can cause even more of the current to flow through your body if a fault develops. For this reason, the grounding wire and its connection should be checked regularly. A receptacle tester can be used to check very

Fig. 5-1. Three-wire plug and receptacle

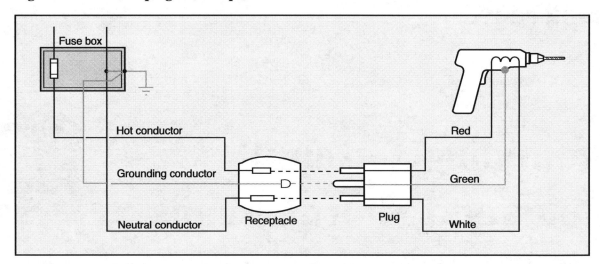

quickly for correct receptacle wiring and grounding. A combination of indicating lights on the plug-in device can reveal a specific problem or indicate a properly wired system. An example is shown in Fig. 5-2.

WARNING

Under no circumstances should the grounding prong be bent or broken off to make a three-prong plug fit into a two-slot receptacle. This unsafe act endangers you and other workers.

Circuit Grounding

5.05   Circuits are grounded to avoid unnecessary and dangerous potential differences between two conducting surfaces. Circuit grounding also limits potential differences that might occur by contact between the circuit and other equipment—values higher than the circuit are designed to withstand.

5.06   To illustrate the need for proper grounding, look at the low-voltage circuit in the diagrams on this page and the following pages. These circuits are typical of those you can expect to find in almost any industrial plant.

5.07   Figure 5-3 is a diagram of a distribution transformer with 120 V service leads. A grounding connection at the service has a

Fig. 5-2. A receptacle tester

Fig. 5-3. Ungrounded conduit

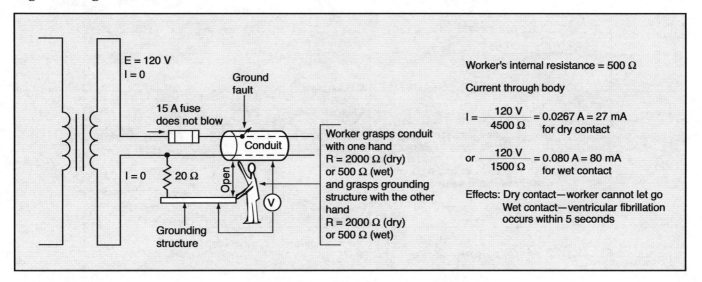

resistance of 20 Ω between the neutral conductor and a *grounding structure*. This grounding structure is not the earth. It might be a metal frame or other structure that is not connected to the earth.

5.08   One conductor from the transformer is equipped with a 15 A fuse. The metal conduit is not connected to the grounding structure, however, so in the diagram the connection between the conduit and the ground is labeled "open."

5.09   Suppose the insulation fails at one point on the 120 V conductor, allowing it to make contact with the conduit. The potential difference between the conduit and the ground is then 120 V. Because the conduit is ungrounded, there is no fault current. The conduit can remain energized at 120 V indefinitely. Anyone making contact between the conduit and ground would experience a shock. You can calculate how serious this shock would be by using Ohm's law.

5.10   In order to calculate how serious the shock would be, you must make certain assumptions. For example, suppose you assume that someone grabs the conduit with one hand while holding onto a grounded structure with the other. Table 5-1 shows the approximate resistance at each contact, and the internal resistance of the worker's body. Figure 5-3 shows the following.

* If the contact is *dry*, the resistance at each hand is about 2000 Ω, making a total resistance of about 4500 Ω (2000 + 2000 + 500).

Table 5-1. Electrical resistance of the human body

Connection	Resistance	
	Dry	Wet
Finger touch......................	40 to 1000 kΩ	4 to 15 kΩ
Hand holding wire.............	15 to 50 k	3 to 6 k
Finger-thumb grasp...........	10 to 30 k	2 to 5 k
Hand holding pliers...........	5 to 10 k	1 to 3 k
Palm touch.......................	3 to 8 k	1 to 2 k
Hand around pipe..............	1 to 3 k	500 to 1500 k
Two hands around pipe.....	500 to 1500 k	250 to 500 k
Hand in water...................	—	200 to 300 k
Foot in water....................	—	100 to 300 k
Internal, excluding skin......	—	200 to 1000 k

Table 5-2. Effects of electric current on the human body

Current	Effects	Feeling or result
0 to 1 mA 1 to 3 mA 3 to 10 mA	None	Imperceptible Mild sensation Painful
10 mA 30 mA 75 mA	Arms paralyzed Breathing muscles paralyzed Causes fibrillation in some people within 5 seconds	Cannot release hand grip Unable to breathe (may be fatal) Heart action becomes uncoordinated (probably fatal)
250 mA	Causes fibrillation in almost everyone within 5 seconds	
4 A	Heart paralysis	Heart stops during shock, but may restart when shock ends (usually not fatal due to heart uncoordination)
More than 5A	Tissues burned	Not fatal, unless vital organs are burned

- If the contact is *wet*, the resistance at each hand may be only 500 Ω, making a total resistance of about 1500 Ω (500 + 500 + 500).

The resistance also depends on how tightly the person grips the metal, and on other factors.

5.11   The resistance of the connection between the neutral conductor and the ground (20 Ω) must be added to the resistance of the body. However, the effect of this resistance is small compared to the resistance of the body, and you can neglect it in this case. The potential difference across the person's body is almost the full 120 V between the two conductors.

5.12   You can use Ohm's law to calculate the current through the worker's body. This calculation is shown in Fig. 5-3. The current is about 27 mA if the contact is dry, and about 80 mA if the contact is wet. From Table 5-2 you can see that even if the contact is dry, the current is high enough to prevent the worker from releasing his grip and breaking the circuit.

Table 5-3. Maximum time without fibrillation

Potential difference	Shock duration
120 V ac	4.2 seconds
240	1.05
277	0.8
480	0.26

For 150 lb human, with resistance of 1500Ω

5.13   From Table 5-3 you can see that if the contact is wet (resistance = 1500 Ω), the worker's heart will go into ventricular fibrillation within about 5 s. The worker will die unless he is released from the electrical path and his heart is restarted within 4 min.

5.14   An improvement in the grounding is shown in Fig. 5-4. The conduit is connected to the ground by a path having a resistance of 10 Ω. How much protection does this path offer?

5.15   If the insulation fails and the 120 V conductor makes contact with the metal conduit, a potential difference of 120 V exists across the path from the conduit to the ground to the opposite side of the transformer. This path has a total resistance of 30 Ω. Therefore, the current in the path is 4 A as shown by the calculation included in Fig. 5-4. As in the first example, this current is not high enough to blow the 15 A fuse.

5.16   The potential difference of 120 V between the two sides of the transformer is now divided into two parts.

- 40 V between the conduit and the grounding structure

- 80 V between the grounding structure and the opposite side of the secondary of the transformer.

5.17   Now suppose the same worker grabs both the conduit and the grounding structure. Under dry conditions, the worker's body creates a path having a resistance of 4500 Ω in parallel with the 10 Ω path. What is the effect on the worker's body?

5.18   The potential difference across the worker's body is limited to 40 V, because of the parallel 10 Ω path from the conduit to the grounding structure. Therefore, the current through the worker's body is only about 9 mA, as shown by the calculations in Fig. 5-4. You can see from Table 5-2 that this current will cause a painful shock, but the worker will be able to let go of the metal structures and break the circuit. Even if the contact is wet, the current will be only about 27 mA (40 V divided by 1500 Ω). This current will prevent the worker from releasing his grip, and breathing may be impossible.

5.19   Finally, suppose the connection from the conduit to the grounding structure is a short length of heavy copper wire, having no resistance, as

Fig. 5-4. Conduit grounded through resistive path

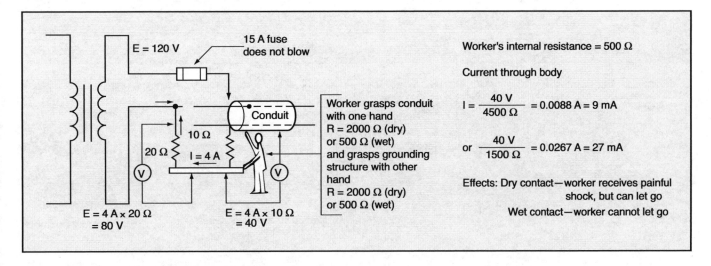

Fig. 5-5. Conduit grounded through 0-ohm path

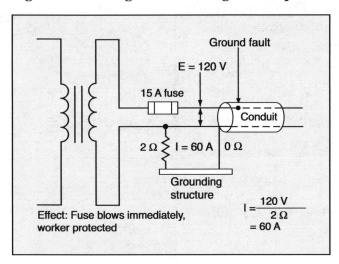

Ground fault

E = 120 V

15 A fuse

Conduit

2 Ω I = 60 A   0 Ω

Grounding
structure

$I = \dfrac{120\ V}{2\ \Omega} = 60\ A$

Effect: Fuse blows immediately, worker protected

shown in Fig. 5-5. In addition, suppose the connection from the grounding structure to the opposite side of the transformer has a resistance of only 2 Ω. What is the effect of an insulation failure in this example?

5.20 If the insulation fails, the potential difference of 120 V is applied across a resistance of only 2 Ω. The current is therefore 60 A, as shown by the calculation in Fig. 5-5. This current quickly blows the 15 A fuse, and disconnects the transformer from the conduit. Anyone who grabs the conduit and the grounding structure under these circumstances will be protected from an electric shock.

5.21 You can see from these examples that proper grounding is very important for the safety of anyone who works or lives around electrical equipment. Proper grounding and overcurrent protection are necessary to disconnect a circuit from the power source quickly if a fault occurs. If grounding is inadequate or nonexistent, a circuit can become lethal if a fault develops.

5.22 The National Electrical Code specifies the minimum provisions necessary for "the practical safeguarding of persons and property from hazards arising from the use of electricity." The *NEC* is a valuable reference tool that contains a great deal of information on the subject of grounding. Whenever you refer to the *NEC*, make sure you have the latest edition. In recent years, it has been published in 2005, 2008, and 2011.

Fig. 5-6. Ground-fault circuit interrupter

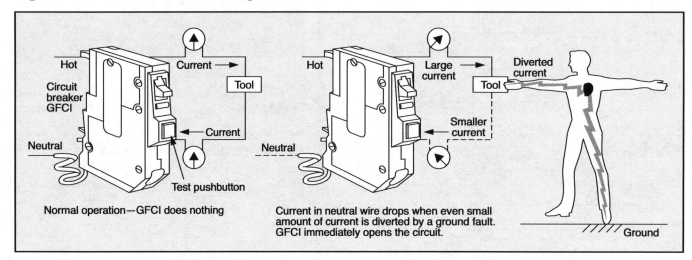

Hot

Current →

Tool

Circuit
breaker
GFCI

Neutral

← Current

Test pushbutton

Normal operation—GFCI does nothing

Hot

Large
current →

Tool

Diverted
current

Smaller
current

Neutral

Current in neutral wire drops when even small amount of current is diverted by a ground fault. GFCI immediately opens the circuit.

Ground

Protection Against Ground Faults

5.23   Depending on conditions and on the nature of the contact, a ground fault has either high or low resistance. When the resistance is low, large amounts of current can flow, blowing the fuse or tripping the circuit breaker. When this happens, the fault current exists only for the very short time that it takes the fuse or circuit breaker to cut off the current in the circuit.

5.24   When the fault circuit has a high resistance, a *ground-fault circuit interrupter* (abbreviated *GFCI*) provides the necessary protection. Under normal conditions, as shown at the left in Fig. 5-6, the current in the two conductors is equal and the GFCI does nothing. However, the instant a ground fault occurs, as shown at the right in the drawing, the current in the two wires becomes unequal. The GFCI compares the current in the two conductors of a circuit. If the currents differ even slightly, as happens when a ground fault allows part of the current to bypass a section of one conductor, the GFCI opens the circuit, thus stopping the flow of all current in the circuit.

5.25   Because the GFCI operates in a split second, it is the *only* method of reliably protecting personnel from injury. Built-in GFCIs have been required in many circuits since about 1970, even if these circuits are also protected by fuses or circuit breakers. Fuses and circuit breakers simply do not respond quickly enough to protect human life. GFCIs generally respond to hot-to-neutral wire faults and line-to-line faults as well as ground faults. They add to the protection offered by fuses and circuit breakers, because they can be tripped by a very small amount of current (as little as 5 mA) acting for only a fraction of a second.

5.26   Some GFCIs are small enough to be carried in a toolbox and plugged in at the point of use. A portable GFCI is shown in Fig. 5-7. Others are installed in the power distribution center. Either type satisfies the *NEC*. Because of the protection they provide, many plants are installing GFCIs in all 120 V circuits, especially those used for portable electric tools. Receptacles installed outdoors or in bathrooms must be equipped with GFCIs. Most GFCI instructions include a simple test procedure involving a pushbutton. To ensure satisfactory operation, it is essential that the manufacturer's test be performed regularly.

Fig. 5-7. Portable GFCI

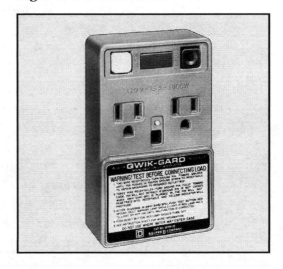

Fig. 5-8. Fault in ungrounded transformer

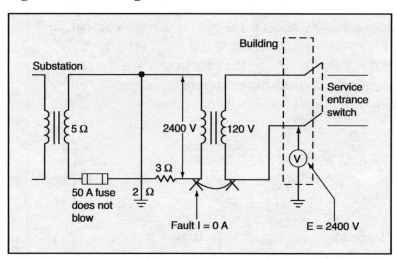

Transformer Grounding

5.27   All the preceding examples involve a branch-circuit ground fault. What happens when a fault develops between the primary and secondary sides of a transformer, as shown in Fig. 5-8? This diagram shows a substation that supplies 2400 V to the building transformers. The transformer in the substation is grounded on its secondary side.

5.28   Suppose a fault occurs between the primary and secondary sides of the building transformer. Because there is no secondary ground on the building transformer, there is no fault current. Instead, the secondary system rises to the potential difference of the primary system—2400 V.

5.29   Figure 5-9 shows the same circuit with two 10 Ω grounds added— a secondary ground on the transformer and a ground on the line side of the service entrance switch. The two 10 Ω grounds in parallel have a combined resistance of 5 Ω. To this resistance you must add the resistance of the substation line and the impedance of the substation transformer.

Two building grounds	5 Ω
Substation line	3 Ω
Substation transformer	5 Ω
Ground connection	2 Ω
Total	15 Ω

5.30   The fault in the building transformer applies a potential difference of 2400 V across this total resistance of 15 Ω. The current is therefore 160 A, as shown by the calculation in Fig. 5-9. The 160 A current far exceeds the rating of the 50 A fuse located in the substation line, and therefore the fuse quickly blows.

Fig. 5-9. Fault in properly grounded transformer

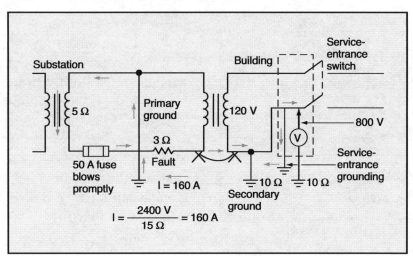

5.31   During the short period of time between the occurrence of the fault and the blowing of the fuse, a potential difference exists between the secondary of the building transformer and the ground. According to Ohm's law, this potential difference is 800 V, not the full 2400 V produced by the transformer. The value is based on a current of 160 A combined with a resistance of 5 Ω.

Effects of Impedance

5.32   In the examples given so far, the fault has been assumed to have no impedance. The following examples are based on the same circuit shown in Fig. 5-9, except that the fault adds an impedance of 30 or 60 Ω.

- If the fault has an impedance of 30 Ω, the total impedance becomes 45 Ω—15 Ω in the distribution circuit and the substation transformer, plus 30 Ω in the fault. In this case, the current in the fault circuit is 53.33 A (2400 V divided by 45 Ω). This current is still high enough to blow the fuse. The potential difference between the building line and ground is 267 V (53.33 A × 5 Ω) until the fuse blows.

- If the fault has an impedance of 60 Ω, the total impedance is 75 Ω. Then the fault current is only 32 A (2400 V divided by 75 Ω), an amount too small to blow the 50 A fuse. A potential difference of 160 V (32 A × 5 Ω) will remain indefinitely between the building line and ground.

5.33   These examples show the value of low impedance in an equipment ground. The lower the impedance, the lower the potential difference that

Fig. 5-10. Grounding low-voltage systems

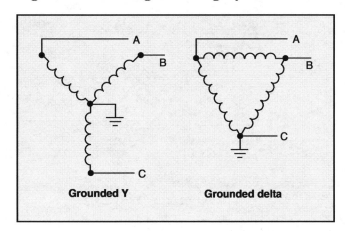

Grounded Y   Grounded delta

can exist from the equipment to ground if a fault occurs.

5.34   Ungrounded low-voltage systems permit primary voltage to appear on the low-voltage wiring under fault conditions. They create a hazard in the normally non-energized metal parts in an electrical system.

5.35   There are two kinds of low-voltage system connections—Y and delta. Each is grounded differently. Both are shown in Fig. 5-10. Each way has its own advantages and disadvantages.

• One of the main advantages of the grounded Y is that the lower potential difference between each phase and the neutral decreases the likelihood of insulation failure. This is particularly true in 480 and 577 V circuits, which operate near the 600 V rating of the insulation on the wire.

• The main disadvantage of the grounded Y is that the protective devices in the system must be equipped with an overcurrent element in each phase to recognize all ground faults.

5.36   The most important feature necessary for adequate equipment grounding is a low-impedance path for the return of the fault current to the source of power. If a low-impedance path is not available, the current may not be high enough to operate the overcurrent devices in the circuit.

5.37   Figure 5-11 shows a grounded Y secondary system with a neutral solidly grounded through a 2 Ω ground. The secondary potential difference is 120/208 V. The load on the branch circuit is protected by 50 A fuses, and the load is grounded separately through a 22 Ω ground connection. There is no ground connection between the transformer and the load.

5.38   When the fault occurs in the motor, the 2 Ω ground is connected in series with the 22 Ω

Fig. 5-11. Motor not grounded to transformer

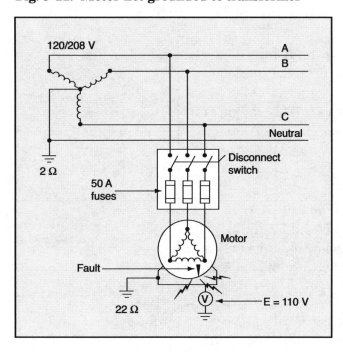

ground, making a total resistance of 24 Ω. The potential difference across this resistance is 120 V, producing a current of 5 A. This current is not sufficient to blow the fuses protecting the motor. Instead, the current maintains a potential difference of 110 V between the motor casing and ground.

5.39   The same circuit is shown in Fig. 5-12, but with an equipment ground between the transformer and the motor. Suppose this line has a resistance of 1 Ω. If the same fault occurs in the motor, it will cause a current of 120 A. This current blows the 50 A fuse and clears the fault from the system. In general, equipment-ground impedance should be low enough to pass a current of at least twice the rating of the overcurrent device at the phase-to-ground potential difference.

Fig. 5-12. Motor grounded to transformer

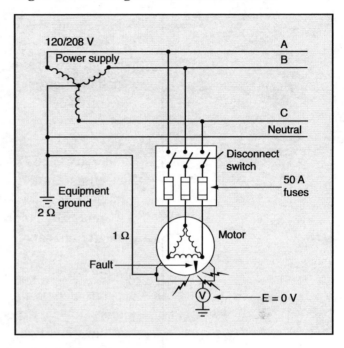

5.40   What apparatus is used in a typical plant to furnish the low-impedance path? Figure 5-13 shows a grounded, Y-connected transformer secondary. The grounding wire is the first link between the transformer and the equipment ground for the plant. The other links shown in the diagram are the equipment-grounding lines.

Fig. 5-13. Links in a grounding system

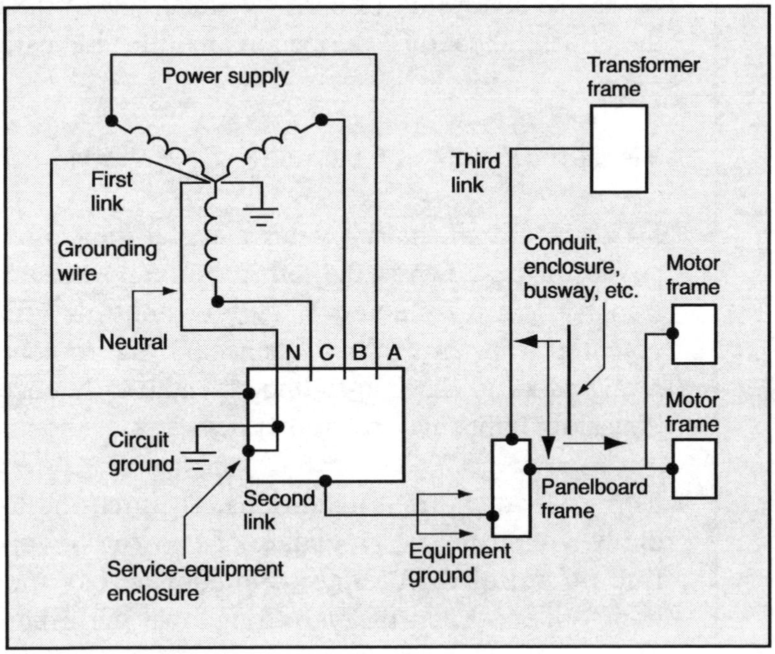

Grounding Through Enclosures

5.41   From the service equipment, the equipment ground is continued by way of conduit or bus-duct enclosure to a panelboard frame. From the panelboard frame, the equipment ground is continued to all the panelboard circuits by means of metallic conduit, bus-duct enclosures, or wire raceways.

5.42   The method of grounding through enclosures is the most commonly used system for equipment grounding today. Tests have shown that either conduit or a busway, installed without a parallel grounding circuit, is an effective equipment ground. Generally, you can assume that any enclosure approved by Underwriters Laboratories Inc. has a low-enough impedance to handle short-circuit fault currents.

5.43   In most cases, equipment that is approved and installed properly is capable of providing a low-impedance grounding path if it has no loose joints. However, periodic inspections may reveal joints in an enclosure that have increased in impedance as a result of vibration, corrosion from nearby chemical processes, or lack of expansion joints. In these cases, you may need to bond the joints. You can bond the joints with a copper wire or other corrosion-resistant material that serves as the bonding jumper.

5.44   You should inspect a busway both during installation and periodically thereafter. The purpose of these inspections is to make sure a low impedance path is maintained throughout the duct enclosure. The inspection should involve testing the resistance of the duct enclosure joints to see that the bolted connections have not developed high resistance as a result of corrosive materials in the plant. One such test is the visual indication described in the following paragraphs.

Visual Indication of Ground for Ungrounded Circuits

5.45   A circuit that provides a visual indication of a grounded phase conductor is shown at the left in Fig. 5-14. It consists of three potential transformers connected Y-Y, with neutrals grounded. Although the potential transformers are connected line-to-neutral, they must have a rating equal to the line-to-line potential difference. Either voltmeters or indicating lights may be used as detectors.

5.46   Under normal conditions, all three indicating lights will glow dimly. Unintentional grounding of one phase will cause the full line-to-line potential difference to appear across the other two potential transformers. Then the indicating light corresponding to the grounded

Fig. 5-14. Ground-indicating circuits

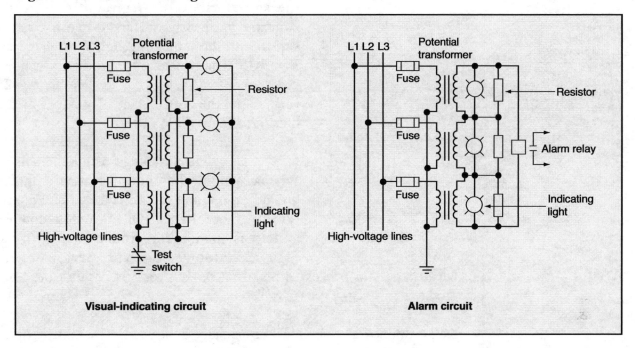

phase will go out, and the lights to the other two phases will glow at their full 120 V brightness.

Grounded Conductor Alarms

5.47   A commonly used circuit that sounds an alarm to indicate a grounded phase conductor is shown by the diagram at the right in Fig. 5-14. This circuit not only provides a visual indication of a grounded conductor (by means of the indicating lights), but also operates a relay that sounds an alarm.

5.48   Each of the three potential transformer primaries is connected from phase to ground. Under normal conditions, the potential difference from the primary to ground equals the line-to-line potential difference divided by the square root of 3. For the circuit shown in Fig. 5-15 on the following page, this value is 120 V divided by the square root of 3, which is about 69 V.

5.49   If one phase becomes grounded, the full line-to-line potential difference appears across the primaries of two potential transformers. The potential difference across the secondary of each potential transformer is 120 V. The potential difference across the open delta, or across the overvoltage relay, is 208 V. This potential difference causes the relay contacts to close and operate the alarm circuit.

Fig. 5-15. Low-voltage ground-detection circuits

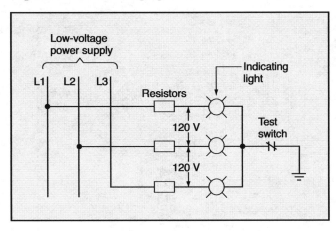

5.50   A low-voltage system (under 600 V) uses the same principle of ground detection. A common, inexpensive method is to use resistors in series with the indicating lights, arranged as in Fig. 5-15. The resistors serve only to reduce the potential difference between the lines to the 120 V rating of the indicating lights. Potential transformers may also be used.

5.51   The main advantage of ground-detection schemes on an ungrounded system is that any ground on the line can be detected and removed rapidly. The alternative is to shut down the system as soon as the ground occurs. In some plants, shutdowns are very serious—either because certain processes must not be stopped, or because the loss of production is very expensive.

5.52   Immediate tripping is especially beneficial. The fault is quickly cleared with a minimum of damage to equipment and system. The ground cannot progress to a more severe line-to-line or multiple fault.

Detecting Ground Faults Automatically

5.53   Three-phase, four-wire Y systems with grounded neutrals offer unmatched safety and protection. A phase-to-ground fault is quickly detected, and the solid neutral ground provides a path for the current necessary to trip protective devices. Every ground fault trips a breaker somewhere in the system. The result is a sudden loss of power to that portion of the system. In many applications, the continuity of service is not essential. In such cases, the Y system is adequate.

5.54   However, in heavy industry (especially in continuous manufacturing processes), service continuity is an important consideration. In these plants, a three-phase, ungrounded delta system is sometimes used.

5.55   A desirable feature of the delta system is its ability to provide normal power to a load with one phase grounded. Since ground faults account for a large portion of electrical trouble, this feature is important in avoiding unexpected power failures. This ability exists only when the system is not already grounded. If one phase of the system has a ground fault, a ground on either of the other two phases will produce ground current, tripping the protective devices. For maximum reliability, ground faults should be repaired immediately.

5.56   Perfect insulation has an infinite resistance. Insulation that has broken down or "faulted" completely has no resistance. Average insulation in a power system falls somewhere between these two extremes. Usual values are in the range of one million to ten million ohms (1 to 10 megohms). A fault exists if the insulation has a low-enough resistance to permit a significant current.

5.57   Insulation seldom breaks down suddenly at operating potential differences. It deteriorates gradually over a period of time. Therefore, it is important to know that the insulation resistance is declining long before the insulation actually fails. With this knowledge, you can schedule repairs in an orderly and economical way.

5.58   In the past, the standard method of monitoring for ground faults was to sense the phase-to-ground potential difference with lamps, meters, or other voltage-sensitive devices. These devices have a number of limitations and are used mainly to indicate a complete breakdown of insulation. These devices do not become sensitive until the insulation resistance has dropped to around 10,000 Ω. Therefore, they give no early warning of insulation deterioration.

5.59   For an accurate check on an electrical system, the common practice is to measure the insulation resistance with dc test equipment. To make these measurements, the power must be shut off and circuits isolated from one another. This procedure is costly, so these measurements are generally made only once a year.

5.60   Readings obtained are of limited value unless they are recorded. They must also be standardized to account for variable conditions, and then compared to previous readings to reveal trends. The best practice is to keep a graph showing the readings for each circuit. An abrupt change in the slope of the graph indicates approaching trouble.

5.61   Because of inadequate methods of detecting faults, many ungrounded three-phase systems actually limp along with undetected ground faults. Thus, one of the main advantages of the ungrounded delta system is lost.

Static Electricity

5.62   The electricity discussed so far in this chapter is called *current electricity*. Current electricity is generated by a source of electrical energy (a battery or generator, for example) and involves the flow of electrons. Virtually all of the electricity that you use is current electricity. Another kind of electricity—*static electricity*—must be covered here briefly

Fig. 5-16. Proper grounding for transfer of flammable liquids

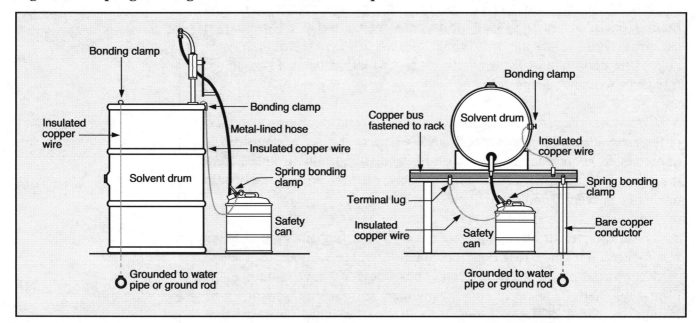

because it is present in almost all industrial operations and manufacturing processes. Static electricity involves charges that remain unmoving on an object.

5.63   Everyone has come into contact with static electricity at one time or another. You have seen signs of its presence when you run a comb through your hair on a dry day. Your hair seems to stand on end and "reach" for the comb. Your hair is actually losing electrons to the comb. Your hair becomes positively charged as a result of this loss of electrons. The comb becomes negatively charged when it gains electrons.

5.64   You can place a charge on yourself by shuffling your feet across a carpeted room on a dry day. This charge will give you a mild shock when you touch a doorknob or other metal object. The electrons that you collected are "jumping" to an object with fewer electrons.

5.65   In most situations, static electricity is more a nuisance than a hazard. Although it is easily generated, static electricity itself is not dangerous either because the charge is weak or because it leaks off as quickly as it is formed. Except for lightening (which is nothing more than a giant static discharge formed in the layers of the earth's atmosphere) no one has ever been killed by a static electricity shock.

5.66   In many situations, it is impossible NOT to generate static electricity. Generation, however, is not the problem—accumulation and discharge are the problems. A static discharge can damage electronic components. It can startle you enough to cause an accident or fall. In some cases, you can see its discharge as a spark. These sparks can easily ignite flammable liquids, vapor, or dusts. Many injuries and millions of dollars of damage occur in industry each year as a result of fires and explosions caused by static electricity.

5.67   As mentioned earlier, static electricity can be generated by friction between two surfaces. It also can be generated by the separation of two unlike materials. A common situation in which static electricity presents a serious hazard is the transfer of flammable liquids from one container to another. The rapid separation that occurs as liquid exits the original container can cause static electricity to be generated.

5.68   Several methods are available for preventing the accumulation of static electricity. Grounding is the most common. Grounding prevents the accumulation of static electricity by channeling it to the ground. Many approved static electricity grounding devices are available. To be effective, a grounding device must be a good conductor of electricity and it must make a path to the earth.

5.69   Figure 5-16 shows containers properly grounded for the transfer of a flammable liquid. The containers must be connected with a ground wire, and at least one of the containers must be connected to a permanent ground. To be effective, complete metal-to-metal contact must be made throughout the grounding system so that any accumulated static reaches the ground. Remove any rust, paint, or other coating that could prevent good contact between the grounding wire and the container.

5.70   It is essential that you ground equipment before you begin the job. Grounding after you have begun the job can cause sparks. In an explosive atmosphere, this action could be disastrous.

5.71   If a fire should occur, it is important that you know how to extinguish it. Water extinguishes many fires by cooling the fuel below the temperature at which it burns. However, water does not extinguish all fires. In fact, water can spread fires involving gasoline, oil, and other chemicals that float on water. Different kinds of fires must be put out in different ways. Table 5-4 lists the four classes of fire extinguishers as well as the types of fires that they are designed to extinguish. The most important thing to remember is this: never attempt to fight a fire that could endanger you. Instead, leave the area immediately and sound the alarm.

Table 5-4. Four classes of fire extinguishers

Class of fire extinguisher	Type of fire
A	Fires in ordinary combustible materials
B	Fires in flammable liquids
C	Fires in energized electrical equipment
D	Fires in combustible metals that can explode, such as lithium (Li), sodium (Na), and potassium (K)

Chapter Six

Fuses and Circuit Breakers

The Purpose of a Fuse

6.01   If a circuit carries too much current, the fuse opens and breaks the circuit. For example, the fuse opens if there is a short circuit. When the fuse opens, the current becomes zero. With zero current, equipment on the line cannot operate. The fuse also opens if there is an overload condition in the equipment or in the line. An overload is a condition in a circuit that causes the current to be too high. The open fuse protects the equipment from being damaged by the overload.

6.02   A fuse is one kind of *overcurrent protective device*. Another common example of such a device is the circuit breaker, which is covered later in this chapter. All overcurrent protective devices protect the circuit, the surrounding materials, and people from being harmed by excess current in the circuit.

6.03   A fuse must do four things in a circuit. It must:

- sense the amount of current in the circuit

- open quickly when the current becomes excessive

- fail to open during a normal temporary overload

- function without affecting the normal operation of the circuit.

Lead-Wire Fuses

6.04   Older fuses were simply pieces of lead wire connected in the circuit. Current in the lead wire raised the temperature of the wire—the higher the current, the higher the temperature. Lead melts at a lower

Fig. 6-1. Cartridge fuses

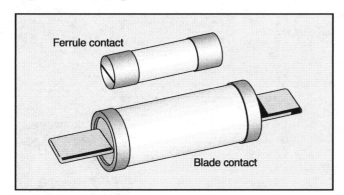

Ferrule contact

Blade contact

Fig. 6-2. Fuse block for cartridge fuse

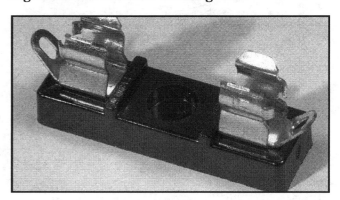

temperature than most metals, so the wire would melt if the current through it became too high.

6.05   The lead wire was kept short and fastened under screws. By selecting wire of the proper diameter, the fuse could be made to open the circuit at any desired current. When a lead fuse blew, molten metal spattered over equipment and people nearby. Lead-wire fuses were also a fire hazard if nothing confined the electric arc that formed as the fuse blew.

Cartridge Fuses

6.06   The cartridge fuse has replaced the old lead-wire fuse. Figure 6-1 shows two kinds of cartridge-fuse construction in use today. Both kinds consist of a hard fiber cylinder surrounding a soft metal fuse strip. This strip is gripped by caps or ferrules on the ends of the fuse chamber. The entire cartridge is mounted in a fuse block. Figure 6-2 shows a fuse block. The cartridge fuse is held in the block by spring clips that grip the ferrules or the knife blades at the ends of the cartridge. The clips simplify the job of replacing a blown fuse.

Fig. 6-3. Renewable-link cartridge fuse

Fig. 6-4. Fuse links

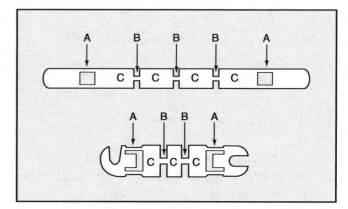

6.07   There are two basic kinds of cartridge fuses—renewable link and one time. Renewable-link fuses have removable end caps so that you can take out the damaged fuse link and replace it after the fuse blows. An example is shown in Fig. 6-3. Renewable-link cartridge fuses have the same general characteristics as one-time fuses. They cost less to replace because the cartridges can be reused. Renewable-link fuses are no longer allowed in most new installations, although link replacement is permitted in existing installations.

6.08   The one-time fuse is sealed by the manufacturer. One-time cartridge fuses offer protection against overloads where the fault current does not exceed 10,000 A. They are commonly used in lighting and heating circuits. The entire fuse must be replaced when it blows.

6.09   Figure 6-4 shows some of the fuse link configurations used in cartridge fuses. Areas A and B are calibrated to melt at a specific current, according to the rating of the fuse. Area C is made of zinc and has a thick cross section. This area absorbs heat to delay the blowing of the fuse and permit momentary overloads. In a circuit with a current in excess of 135% (a light overload), the link will open the areas marked B. In a short circuit or ground fault, the link will open in all areas marked A and B. The sections marked C will drop out in their original metallic form.

Dual-Element Cartridge Fuses

WARNING

Always use nonconductive fuse tongs when removing or installing cartridge fuses.

6.10   Dual-element cartridge fuses are designed mainly for motor circuit protection. The construction of this kind of cartridge fuse is shown in Fig. 6-5. The fuse blows when either of the two elements inside opens. For overloads, the opening of the fuse is achieved by the melting of a time-delay element made from an alloy. For short circuits, links on either end of the fuse blow in a fraction of an ac cycle.

Fig. 6-5. Dual-element cartridge fuse

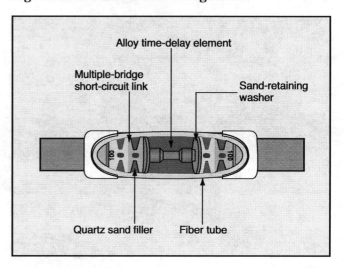

Alloy time-delay element

Multiple-bridge short-circuit link

Sand-retaining washer

Quartz sand filler   Fiber tube

Fig. 6-6. Action of a dual-element fuse

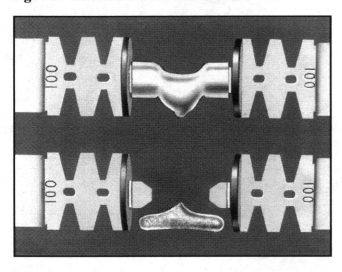

6.11   The alloy used in the overload element melts at less than half the temperature increase required to melt the zinc links. Both excess current and a specific time period are required for this element to reach its melting point. If an overload persists, or if the magnitude of the overload increases, the alloy melts instantly without passing through a half-melted state. The alloy retains its shape and strength up to the point of becoming liquid. This action is shown in Fig. 6-6.

6.12   When a short circuit occurs, the fuse links open the circuit immediately. The calibrated links have a series of melt bridges that blow when a fault occurs. Multiple bridges in the links cause the wider sections to drop out. These are replaced by quartz sand, which interrupts the arc quickly.

6.13   Dual-element fuses have several advantages over single-element fuses:

- They can be selected to match the actual motor running current closely because they do not blow on harmless momentary overloads. Therefore, there is less nuisance blowing.

- Their low let-through current prevents the fault current from reaching destructive levels in the more vulnerable branch circuits and associated equipment. This would be less possible with ordinary single-element fuses or where more costly fuses are not justified.

- They can be more closely matched to the protective wiring and equipment because they are not subject to nuisance blowing. Therefore, the equipment used can be more compact and less expensive.

- They are ideally suited for protection of coils, relays, solenoids, and other magnetic equipment because the time-delay element will not blow on the momentary in-rush current. Yet, they will blow if the overload is sustained.

Current-Limiting Fuses

6.14   Underwriters Laboratories describes a current-limiting fuse as one that starts to melt within 90 electrical degrees of a short circuit, and will open the circuit within 180 electrical degrees (half a cycle). Thus, a current-limiting fuse acts faster than an ordinary fuse. It limits the peak let-through current, therefore limiting the amount of energy allowed into the circuit.

6.15   High-capacity systems can produce extremely high fault currents. High fault currents can cause violent arcing and burning at the point of fault. They can bend copper bars in bus ducts and switchboards, melt and explode thermal overload units of combination starters, and weld contacts of motor controls. Current-limiting fuses interrupt the circuit very quickly, thus limiting energy let-through. Most fuses used in modern systems are current limiting.

Fig. 6-7. Power fuse

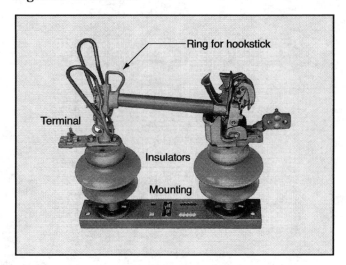

Power Fuses

6.16   Power fuses are designed for use in high-voltage installations. The potential differences range from 2300 to 30,000 V or more, depending on the power company. A typical power fuse is shown in Fig. 6-7.

6.17   Power fuses are used in load-interrupter circuits and are available in current-limiting or noncurrent-limiting types. Current-limiting fuses reduce the energy let-through. Two kinds of noncurrent-limiting power fuses are made. They operate in different ways.

- *Expulsion fuses* expel hot gases when they blow. This type of fuse should not be used indoors because of the hazard presented by the expelled gases. The *NEC* requires that expulsion fuses be designed to prevent any hazard to people or property.

- *Nonexpulsion fuses* have condensers or other protection against arcing and gas expulsion.

Cartridge Fuse Classes, Sizes, and Ratings

6.18   Cartridge fuses come in a wide range of types, sizes, and ratings. Various classes are designated by NEMA (National Electrical Manufacturers Association) and UL standards. Present NEMA and UL standards classify standard *NEC* one-time or renewable-cartridge fuses as Class H. These fuses are classified at interrupting ratings of up to 10,000 A.

Fig. 6-8. Cartridge fuses

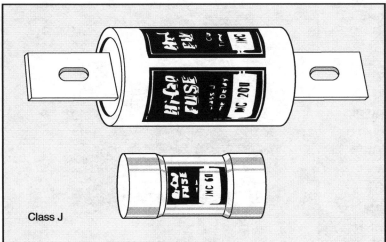

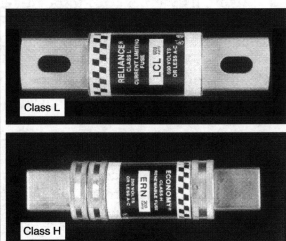

6.19   Cartridge-fuse classifications based on existing UL requirements at IC (interrupting capacity) ratings above 10,000 A RMS are Class J, L, G, or K. These fuses are called high-interrupting-capacity fuses, indicating an interrupting rating at some value between 10,000 and about 300,000 A RMS. Class J and Class L fuses are current-limiting, high-interrupting-capacity fuses. The interrupting ratings are marked on the label.

6.20   Class J fuse dimensions are different from standard Class H cartridge fuses of the same voltage and current ratings. They require special fuseholders that will not accept noncurrent-limiting fuses. This requirement complies with *NEC* Article 240.60(B), which reads in part, "Fuseholders for current-limiting fuses shall not permit insertion of fuses that are not current-limiting." Class J fuses of 60 A or less are ferrule types. Nonferrule types, from 60 to 600 A, have slots in the fuse knife blades to permit bolted or knife-blade connections to fuseholders, as shown in Fig. 6-8.

6.21   Class L fuses are divided into several current classifications, with various blade mounting hole dimensions. The dimensions vary according to fuse size, permitting bolted connection to fuseholders. An example is shown in Fig. 6-8.

6.22   Class K fuses have interrupting ratings of 50,000 to 200,000 A RMS at various peak let-through currents and maximum let-through energy conditions. These fuses are divided into three groups—K1, K5, and K9.

6.23   All fuses presently listed as UL Class K have the same dimensions as conventional Class H 250 V or 600 V, 0 to 600 A fuses. An example of a Class H fuse is shown in Fig. 6-8. Because of this interchangeable feature, Class K fuses are not labeled current limiting, even though qualifications for K1 fuses closely match the qualifications for Class J fuses.

Installing Cartridge Fuses

6.24   Sometimes fuses require the use of switching devices. The *NEC* requires that a means of disconnecting be provided on the supply side of all fuses and thermal cutouts in circuits of more than 150 V to ground. A disconnect is also required for all cartridge fuses in circuits (of any voltage) where the fuses are accessible to anyone other than qualified persons.

6.25   Spring clips for ferrule or knife-blade fuses should make a tight contact with fuse terminals over a large area. Do not use damaged clips that cannot provide a good contact surface with the fuse. Follow these suggestions when you insert a fuse into a clip.

WARNING

Never insert fuses in a live circuit. The arcing that results can burn, gouge, or weld the ferrule or knife blade, reducing the effective contact between the fuse and the clip.

- Keep fuse clips, fuse ferrules, and blades clean and smooth across the contact surface. If necessary, use a non-abrasive cleaner to clean contacting parts. Never use sandpaper or other abrasives.

- A ferrule-type cartridge fuse cannot be rotated easily in its clip if the contact is tight. A knife-blade cartridge fuse is difficult to insert if the spring clips make tight contact.

- If spring clips lose their tension or gripping strength, you should replace them. Clamping devices are available to provide tight connection between the fuseholder and the fuse.

6.26   *NEC* rules on installation of fuses include the following:

- Generally, overcurrent devices (fuses) must be installed so that they are readily accessible. That is, they must be capable of being reached quickly for operation, renewal, or inspection, without requiring those who must have ready access to climb over or remove obstacles, or to resort to portable ladders. An exception to this rule is made when an overcurrent device is used in a busway plug-in unit to tap a branch circuit from the busway.

- Overcurrent devices must be enclosed in cutout boxes or cabinets, unless they are a part of a specially approved assembly which provides equivalent protection.

Fig. 6-9. Edison-base plug fuse

Fig. 6-10. Type S plug fuse and adapter

• Enclosures for overcurrent devices in damp or wet locations must be of a type approved for such locations and must be mounted so there is at least ¼ in. (6 mm) of air space between the enclosure and the vertical surface on which it is mounted.

• Enclosures for overcurrent devices must be mounted vertically, unless this is impractical.

• Fuses must be located or shielded so that people will not be burned or otherwise injured by fuse operation.

• Although the Code gives maximum heights at which overcurrent protective devices are considered readily accessible, an overcurrent device with a center no more than 6½ ft (2 m) above the floor or working platform will be satisfactory to most regulating authorities.

Plug Fuses

6.27   A plug fuse has a threaded base that screws into a socket. A familiar household example is shown in Fig. 6-9. This kind of fuse is called the Edison-base plug fuse. The plug fuse is usually satisfactory only for home lighting and heating circuits.

6.28   Article 240.50 of the *NEC* says that "Plug fuses and fuseholders shall not be used in circuits exceeding 125 V between conductors." An exception allows their use in circuits having a grounded neutral and no conductor at over 150 V to ground.

6.29   Rarely do you have a branch circuit on which a motor is never connected. With a motor on the circuit, the ordinary plug fuse is not satisfactory. It has very little time delay, and the starting current of any motor will often blow the fuse, especially if the circuit is already partially loaded. Fluorescent lighting often brings about the same condition because of the high starting current.

6.30   The dual-element plug fuse eliminates such unnecessary fuse blowing. The dual-element plug fuse works on the same principle as the dual-element cartridge fuse.

Fig. 6-11. Glass-tube fuses

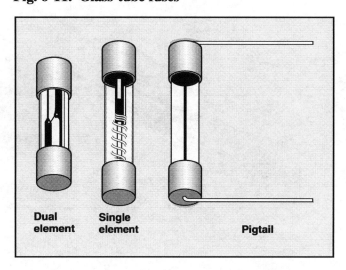

Dual element   Single element   Pigtail

6.31   Type S fuses are made so that you cannot install a fuse with too large a capacity. Thus, bridging and tampering is practically impossible when this kind of fuse is used. The Type S fuse has the same electrical features as an ordinary plug or dual-element cartridge fuse. Type S fuses can be installed in any Edison-base fuseholder by using a screw-in adapter that locks in place. An example of this fuse and adapter is shown in Fig. 6-10. One adapter is for fuses of 0 to 15 A, a second is for fuses of 16 to 20 A, and a third is for fuses of 21 to 30 A. Type S fuses will not fit adapters of the wrong size.

6.32   Articles 240.50 through 240.54 of the *NEC* define the minimum standards for plug fuses and fuseholders. Note that the Edison-base fuse is mentioned only as a replacement item in existing installations. The Type S fuse shall be used in new installations of up to 30 A.

Glass-Tube Fuses

6.33   Glass-tube fuses are used as supplementary protection for fixtures and equipment. They are used in test equipment to protect the meter circuit. They are also used in automotive circuits and in low-voltage control circuits operating at voltages of less than 250 V. Single-element, dual-element, and pigtail glass-tube fuses are shown in Fig. 6-11.

6.34   Some glass-tube fuses have metal end caps that fit into a fuseholder. However, the pigtail fuse has two leads that are soldered directly into a circuit. The pigtail fuse is a type of single-element fuse.

6.35   Special fuseholders available for use with glass-tube fuses include the spring-clip type and the tubular type. With the tubular type, the fuse is inserted in a plastic tube. A cap is placed over the top and twisted to lock it in place. Both kinds of fuseholders are shown in Fig. 6-12, on the following page.

Fig. 6-12. Glass-tube fuseholders

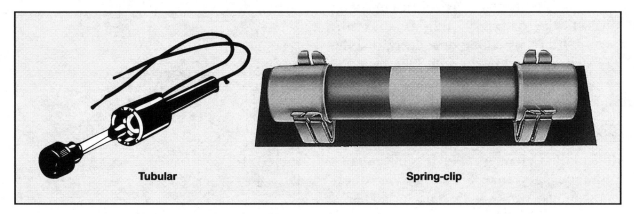

Tubular   Spring-clip

6.36   Two kinds of glass-tube fuses are available.

• A single-element fuse blows instantly when an overload or a short circuit occurs.

• A dual-element fuse has a time-delay element. This element allows a brief overload in the circuit before the fuse blows. Typically, dual-element fuses are used in circuits containing fractional-horsepower motors, relays, and solenoids.

6.37   Supplementary overcurrent protection is used in appliances or other equipment to provide individual protection for specific components. Such protection is not branch circuit protection, and the *NEC* does not require supplemental overcurrent protective devices to be readily accessible for maintenance.

6.38   Typical examples of supplemental overcurrent protection include fuses installed in fluorescent lighting fixtures, movie projectors, and cooking and heating equipment. Fuses used for supplemental overcurrent protection are rated lower than the fuses for the branch circuit supplying the equipment as a whole.

Kinds of Circuit Breakers

6.39   A circuit breaker resembles an automatic light switch. It cuts off the current when it becomes too great. Some circuit breakers have a trip-indicator window that will show a red flag when the breaker is tripped. Most breakers trip to a central lever position. Once the cause of the overload has been corrected, the breaker must be reset by switching it to the OFF position, then ON.

6.40   A circuit breaker is a device for interrupting the current in a circuit under normal or abnormal conditions. Under normal continuous-current rating, a circuit breaker is a single switching device. When the current exceeds the normal rating, either on overload or short circuit, the circuit breaker acts as an automatic overcurrent protective device.

6.41   The function of the circuit breaker is equivalent to the function of a switch in combination with a fuse. The selection and application of circuit breakers depends upon understanding the characteristics of available types and their accessory devices.

6.42   A circuit breaker (sometimes abbreviated CB) automatically interrupts the current when the conditions are abnormal. Unlike a fuse, however, the circuit breaker operates without damage to itself. The circuit breaker mechanism is set to interrupt the current at a specific overload value. It can also interrupt a short-circuit current. In contrast, a manual switch will not automatically interrupt a short-circuit current.

6.43   The automatic action of a circuit breaker can be accomplished in several ways. The most common ways are:

- magnetic action

- a combination of thermal release and magnetic action

- hydraulic or pneumatic means.

Magnetic Circuit Breakers

6.44   A magnetic circuit breaker is used in circuits that must open immediately when a fault occurs. A simple diagram of the magnetic circuit breaker is shown in Fig. 6-13. The diagram at the left shows the circuit breaker under normal conditions. The diagram at the right shows how the circuit breaker trips when the current becomes too high.

Fig. 6-13. Magnetic circuit breaker

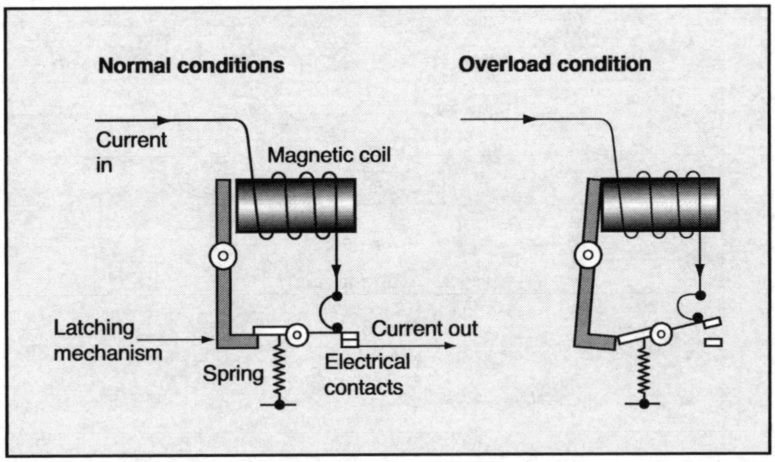

Thermal-Magnetic Circuit Breakers

6.45   The combination circuit breaker has both a thermal strip and a magnetic coil. The thermal strip provides a time delay for small, momentary overloads. The magnetic coil provides instantaneous trip on high overloads or short-circuit currents. The magnetic coil also protects the bimetallic strip from overheating.

6.46   Figure 6-14 is a simple diagram of the thermal-magnetic circuit breaker. The diagram at the left shows the circuit breaker during normal operation. The diagram at the right shows the circuit breaker as it trips and interrupts the circuit.

Ambient-Compensated Circuit Breakers

6.47   The ambient-compensated circuit breaker has two bimetallic strips. They are connected physically so that one strip compensates for changes in the ambient temperature. Thus, the action of the circuit breaker depends only on the temperature increase due to the current and not on the temperature of the surroundings.

6.48   The action of this circuit breaker is shown in Fig. 6-15. You can see that both bimetallic strips bend with an increase in ambient temperature, but only the overload element responds to the current. The circuit breaker trips only when the excessive current through the overload strip causes it to bend more than the compensating strip.

6.49   The ambient-compensated circuit breaker is used in areas where high temperatures occur. Examples include areas where metals are melted, areas near ovens, and boiler rooms.

Fig. 6-14. Thermal-magnetic circuit breaker

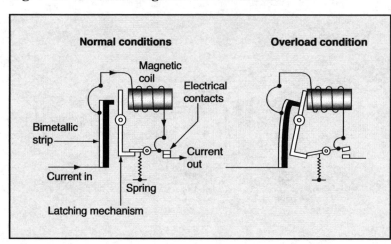

Fig. 6-15. Ambient-compensated circuit breaker

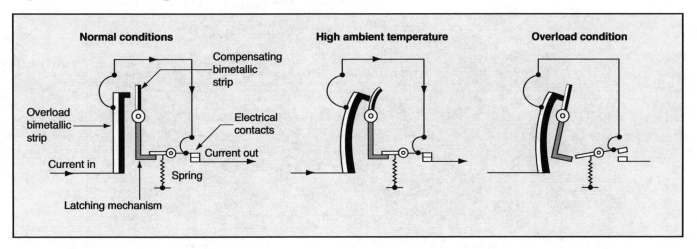

Molded-Case Circuit Breakers

6.50   The molded case of a circuit breaker provides the physical means of positioning the breaker components, and it protects the working parts from damage and contamination. The molded case also protects people from contact with energized components in the breaker. Figure 6-16 shows the internal view of a molded-case circuit breaker.

6.51   A wide range of molded-case circuit breakers is available, with many options. Some examples are shown in Fig. 6-17, on the following page. For example, some circuit breakers provide short-circuit protection only. These breakers can be used on motor circuits where overload protection is provided by the motor starter or built into the motor.

6.52   Molded-case circuit breakers can be used in any low-voltage (less than 600 V) electrical circuit where protection is required, including main service and feeders as well as branch circuits. They are found in switchboards, panelboards, control centers, combination starters, and in individual enclosures.

6.53   Potential difference is the most important consideration in selecting a molded-case circuit breaker. Devices for ac service are available in ratings of 120/240, 240, 277, 480, and 560 V. Molded-case breakers for dc service are available in 120 and 240 V ratings.

6.54   The interrupting ability of molded-case circuit breakers is greater on ac than on dc. For

Fig. 6-16. Molded-case circuit breaker

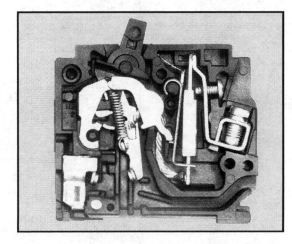

Fig. 6-17. Typical molded-case circuit breakers

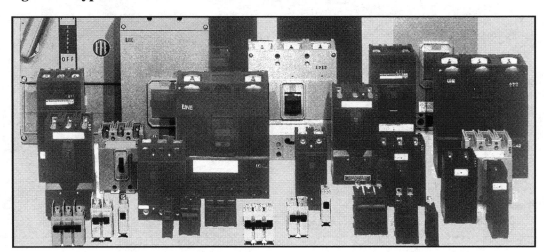

example, a 560 V circuit breaker may have an interrupting capacity of 15,000 A ac at the rated potential difference. When used in a 250 V dc circuit, however, the same circuit breaker can interrupt only 10,000 A.

6.55   *Interrupting capacity* is the fault current a circuit breaker can interrupt without damage to itself. Circuit breakers can be rated at anywhere from 5,000 through 150,000 A of interrupting capacity. If equipped with current-limiting devices, a circuit breaker's interrupting capacity can be increased to 200,000 A. The breaker must be rated for sufficient interrupting capacity to interrupt the maximum amount of current the electrical system can deliver under "bolted-fault" (short-circuit) conditions.

6.56   Where a molded-case circuit breaker is used for motor branch-circuit protection, its rating cannot be less than 115% of motor full-load current rating. However, enough time delay must be provided to start the motor. This provision usually requires using a breaker rated at 150 to 250% of the motor's full-load current. In such an application, the breaker serves both as the disconnect switch and as the fault protection for all circuit components.

6.57   Remember that circuit breakers are basically protective devices rather than service equipment. A circuit breaker's mechanical life is rated in thousands of operations, rather than hundreds of thousands. Applications where a large number of mechanical operations is required should be reviewed to see if a contactor can be placed between breaker and load to perform repetitive mechanical operations.

6.58   Molded-case breakers are relatively trouble-free devices, requiring little maintenance. For the most part, the only maintenance required is to see that all conductor terminals are tight and free from corrosion, and that the breaker is dry and free from accumulated dirt and dust.

6.59   Most circuit breakers require no internal servicing. An exception is the trip unit on breakers in large frame sizes, which is replaceable. Periodic inspection should be made to make sure the trip unit's hold-down bolts are tight.

6.60   Molded-case circuit breakers should be kept clean so that heat can be dissipated properly. Do not break any seals on these units. Electrical connections must be kept tight so that heat is not introduced to the thermal overload element.

6.61   A molded-case circuit breaker consists essentially of two separate elements:

- **A set of contacts.** The contacts are connected to a mechanical linkage for manual operation as a switch.

- **An overload-sensing device.** Normally, the time-delay overload device is thermal, and the instantaneous overload device (if any) is magnetic.

6.62   Manually opening and closing the main contacts of the circuit breaker will not move any of the mechanical joints in the overload device. After a period of inactivity these become stiff or inoperable. The only way to check this condition and eliminate the stiffness is to trip the breaker electrically. You may need to trip the breaker as often as every six months, or as seldom as every few years. The frequency depends on conditions where the breaker is installed.

6.63   Periodically, a molded-case circuit breaker should be subjected to a current equal to 300% of the breaker rating. You should measure the time it takes for this current to trip the breaker, and compare it to the time specified by the manufacturer. If the circuit breaker has an instantaneous element, you should check it for pickup according to the manufacturer's specifications.

Low-Voltage Power Circuit Breakers

6.64   A low-voltage power circuit breaker operates at 600 V or less. The air power circuit breaker shown in Fig. 6-18, on the following page, can be used in an electric circuit to interrupt fault currents, to provide overload protection, or to open and close the electric circuit. A low-voltage power circuit breaker has two elements:

Fig. 6-18. Air power circuit breaker

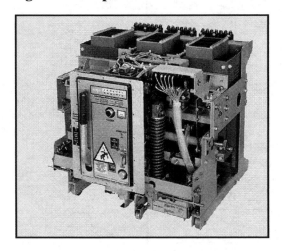

- a set of contacts with a mechanical linkage to open or close the electric circuit rapidly

- an abnormal-condition-sensing element, called a *trip device.*

6.65 This circuit breaker can be equipped with accessories to provide electrical operation, remote operation, reverse-current tripping, shunt tripping, and under-voltage tripping. It may have auxiliary contacts for alarms or indicating lamps. Low-voltage power circuit breakers may have continuous-load ratings of 15 to 6000 A. Interrupting capacities range from 15,000 to 130,000 A at 240 V ac.

6.66 An overload-series tripping device is sometimes magnetic. In these devices, time delay is accomplished by using a dashpot or a ratchet device. Current in the trip coil attracts the armature. The dashpot slows the motion of the armature, producing a time-delayed tripping action. However, these magnetic devices have largely been replaced by electronic units.

6.67 Low-voltage circuit breakers are available with several kinds of resetting devices. One of these devices is the stored-energy mechanism. This mechanism has springs that are compressed either manually or electrically to provide quick reclosing of the breaker contacts. The high-speed closing extends contact life by reducing arcing during reclosing of the contacts.

6.68 The stored-energy mechanism of the air breaker shown in Fig. 6-19 has a mechanism that compresses a spring. The spring stores enough energy to close and latch the breaker. The spring is held in its fully compressed position by a latch until the latch is released for the closing operation. The spring then drives the breaker contacts closed.

6.69 One of the support points of the closing mechanism is a roller that is held in place by a trip latch. Release of this latch allows the mechanism to collapse. The breaker contacts then open and cannot be reclosed except by the action of the compressed spring. The spring cannot expand and close the breaker contacts unless the operator has taken action to compress it.

6.70 A manual spring-driven circuit breaker has a handle on the front to compress the spring. An indicator on the circuit breaker indicates "Spring Charged" when the spring is compressed and able to close the breaker contacts. The breaker may then be manually closed by pushing a close button. It may be electrically closed by a remote contact, which energizes a latch-release coil.

6.71   Some circuit breakers are equipped with a fractional-horsepower, high-speed universal motor and a ratchet mechanism to compress the springs. The compression takes about one second. The motor drives a gear-and-ratchet unit that delivers high torque to the spring-compressing mechanism. The contact-closing operation works only after the spring is fully compressed. The operation can be controlled electrically from a remote source or manually by a close button on the circuit breaker itself.

Circuit Breaker Tripping

6.72   A series trip is a direct-acting tripping device. It actually carries the load current and normally uses the magnetic attraction of a plunger or armature to trip the circuit breaker. The magnetic attraction is slowed by a dashpot to achieve a time-delay operation. Series trip devices have largely been replaced by electronic trip devices.

Fig. 6-19. Stored-energy mechanism

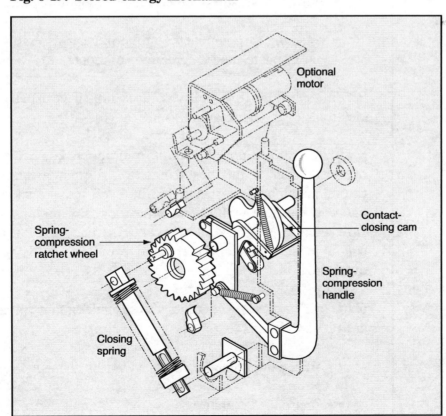

6.73   A circuit breaker tripping device can be equipped to provide three time-current characteristics, either singly or in combination. The three characteristics are listed below:

- **Long time delay.** This characteristic is designed to provide ordinary overload protection. The tripping time is measured in seconds or minutes.

- **Short time delay.** This characteristic is designed for protecting against fault currents and short circuits. The tripping time is measured in numbers of ac cycles.

- **Instantaneous trip.** This characteristic provides instantaneous short-circuit protection. There is no time delay.

6.74   Causes of malfunction of the circuit breaker time-delay components depend on time and severity of duty. Common causes of malfunction generally fall into the following three categories for series devices:

- loss of oil or air seal in the dashpot, physical damage, aging of seals, or physical wear

- clogging of parts (orifices) by foreign matter or oil sludge that forms as a result of environmental conditions and aging of oil

- freezing of components in the plunger assembly due to corrosive atmospheres and long periods of inoperation.

When electronic time-delay devices fail, it is usually the result of an electronic component failure.

6.75   Of all the possible faults, improper delay in opening when an overload occurs is the most dangerous. Normal operating procedures and careful maintenance inspections will reveal most of the conditions that are likely to interfere with circuit protection. But the only way to know for sure whether the circuit breaker will recognize an abnormal circuit condition and operate properly is to test it. The test is done by creating an overload.

6.76   The following conditions may render a low-voltage circuit breaker unfit for service:

- frozen or jammed contacts and/or mechanism

- improper calibration

- improperly set trip element

- high contact resistance

- mechanical linkage problems

- open contacts or damaged series relay

- high resistance or arcing fault, often caused by loose or improper fit between primary fingers and bus contacts

- broken or cracked arc chutes

- loose parts

- accumulated dirt

- contaminated dashpot oil

- electronic component failure.

These can be caused by a variety of conditions, including moisture, corrosion, abuse, wear, vibration, and improper maintenance.

Circuit Breaker Reset and Fuse Replacement

6.77   The proper selection of current-limiting fuses and circuit breakers is essential in electrical systems. If they are to function as designed, fuses must always be replaced with the type and size recommended by the equipment manufacturer.

6.78   When a fuse blows or a circuit breaker trips, something is wrong. Usually it is an overloaded circuit, a short circuit, or a ground fault. Never try to start the current in the circuit flowing again until the problem has been corrected. Many serious accidents have occurred because hidden damage to the electrical system was not corrected before the system was re-energized. Determine the source of the problem and remedy the situation. A brief procedure for following up the trip of a circuit breaker follows.

6.79   If the circuit breaker protecting a motor control circuit has tripped, a fault has occurred and the excess current might have damaged the motor controller. To ensure future safe operation, several steps should be taken by a qualified person before the system is returned to service. These steps are as follows:

1. Turn off and lock out all power supplying the equipment. There may be more than one power supply to be turned off.

2. Examine the circuit breaker for external evidence of damage. (Most circuit breakers are sealed and cannot be examined internally.) Follow the circuit breaker manufacturer's instructions or the NEMA standards for circuit breakers.

3. Inspect all terminals and conductors for discoloration, melting, or other signs of arcing, and replace all damaged parts.

4. Inspect the motor starter for damage to its contacts, contact springs, insulation system, electrical connections, overload relay, and other parts. Replace the overload relay if burnout of the heater element has occurred.

5. After replacing all damaged equipment, inspect the motor controller and manually check all moving parts for freedom of motion.

Chapter Seven

Motor Protection

The Importance of Motor Protection

7.01 Many different kinds of motors have been developed for many different purposes. Their characteristics vary greatly.

- One kind of motor needs 56 seconds starting time under normal load.

- An oil-well pump motor will suffer serious damage if its rotor locks and the motor is not disconnected from the line within 20 seconds.

- A conveyor-drive motor in a potash processing plant can withstand 35% overload for 30 minutes.

- A hermetic compressor motor may burn up in 3 minutes at a 25% overload.

In each example, the motor requires overload protection. The protective device must allow for the starting-current requirements of each motor, but it must also meet the requirement for protection against excessive overload currents.

7.02 Many applications require special motors that in turn require special protective schemes. Even when familiar "standard" motors are used, it is important to select the proper means of protection.

Motor Feeder Protection

7.03 Figure 7-1, on the following page, is a simple diagram of a typical motor circuit. The first protective device is the motor feeder protection.

Fig. 7-1. Motor circuit protective devices

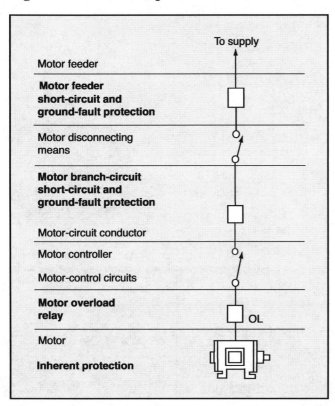

The size of this protective device depends on the number of motors to be connected and their sizes.

7.04   If only one motor is connected, the motor feeder protective device is rated the same as the branch-circuit protective device. However, if more than one motor is connected to the feeder, the rating of the feeder protection is determined as explained on the following page:

- Find the highest permitted fuse capacity for all the motors in the circuit. To do this, multiply the full-load current rating of each motor by the percentage listed for that motor in Table 430.52 of the *National Electrical Code*. Notice that the multiplier depends on the kind of fuse to be installed.

- To the highest current requirement for one motor in the circuit, add the full-load current ratings for all the other motors in the circuit.

7.05   The resulting value is the current rating required for the feeder. If there is no standard-size fuse of that rating, Article 430.62 of the *NEC* requires using a fuse of the next lower rating. The *NEC* permits using a fuse with a higher rating in a motor branch circuit if two or more motors must be started at the same time. However, note that larger feeders must be installed to carry the higher current safely.

7.06   For example, suppose you have a feeder that supplies four 480 V three-phase motors of different sizes, as shown in Fig. 7-2. What is the rating of the proper fuses to use in protecting the feeder circuit?

7.07   The full-load current ratings for the motors are listed in Table 430.250 of the *NEC*. The values are as follows:

> 20 hp, three-phase 480 V. . . . . 27 A
> 10 hp, three-phase 480 V. . . . . 14 A
> 5 hp, three-phase 480 V. . . . . 7.6 A

Both 20 hp motors draw the same full-load current, but they are treated differently in this problem. For one, you add the fuse rating. For the other, you add the full-load current rating.

Fig. 7-2. Motor branch-circuit conductors and protective devices

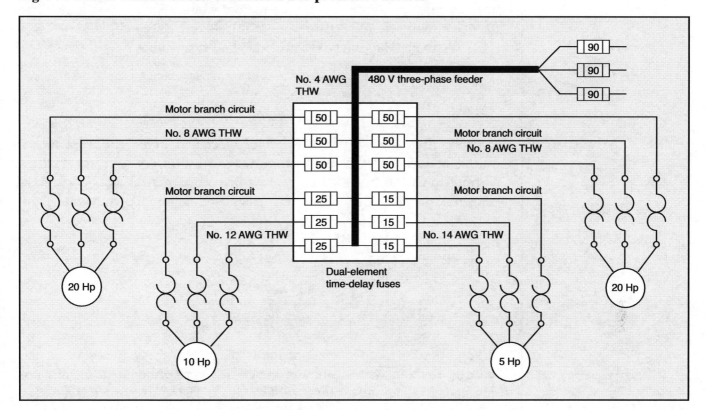

7.08   From Table 430.52, you can see that the multiplying factor for a squirrel-cage motor is 175%, if you use dual-element fuses. Therefore, the current requirement for the fuse is 47.25 A for starting this motor.

$$27 \text{ A} \times 175\% = 47.25 \text{ A}$$

Article 430.52 of the *NEC* permits using a 50 A fuse for this motor.

7.09   In order to calculate the correct current rating of the fuse, add this 50 A to the full-load current rating of all the other motors on the feeder.

20 hp	=	50.00 A
20 hp	=	27.00 A
10 hp	=	14.00 A
5 hp	=	7.60 A
Total	=	98.60 A

There is no standard fuse rated at 98.6 A. The *NEC* requires using the next lower-rated standard fuse in this feeder circuit. The correct fuse is rated at 90 A.

7.10   Note that the full-load current of only one 20 hp motor was multiplied by 175%—not both. However, if both 20 hp motors were required to start at the same time, you would have multiplied both full-load currents by 175%. Then both motors would require 50 A fuses. The feeder circuit would then require a 110 A fuse (50 + 50 + 14 + 7.6 = 121.6 A, reduced to the next lower standard fuse value).

Feeder Size

7.11   Article 430.24 of the *National Electrical Code* requires a feeder rating of 125% of the full-load current of the motor with the highest current, plus the full-load current of the other motors. In the example shown in Fig. 7-2, the feeder size is calculated in the following way:

20 hp motor (1.25 × 27)	=	33.75 A
20 hp motor	=	27 A
10 hp motor	=	14 A
5 hp motor	=	7.60 A
Total	=	82.35 A

7.12   The correct feeder conductor size is No. 4 AWG copper, if the wire is covered with insulation coded THW (thermoplastic insulation, resistant to heat and water). Table 310.15(B)(16) of the *NEC* lists the allowable current for this conductor as 85 A.

7.13   If both 20 hp motors must be able to be started together, the required capacity of the feeder would be 89.1 A. In this case, the next size conductor would be required—No. 3 AWG copper, covered with THW insulation. The allowable current for this conductor, listed in Table 310.15(B)(16), is 100 A.

7.14   The *NEC* provides for determining the current requirements of motors of various sizes. Whenever the full-load current rating of a motor is used for determining the current capacity of overcurrent devices, conductors, and switches, you should use the values listed in *NEC* Tables 430.247 through 430.250.

Branch Circuits

7.15   A *branch circuit* is the portion of a wiring system that extends from the final overcurrent device to the outlet. A device not approved for branch-circuit protection—a thermal cutout or a motor overload protective device, for example—is not considered to be an overcurrent device

Fig. 7-3. Branch-circuit protection

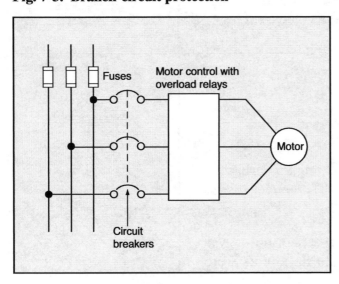

protecting the circuit. Figure 7-3 is a simple diagram of a branch circuit. The circuit breakers are the final overcurrent devices protecting the circuit. The motor control box has overload relays for motor protection, but they are not overload protective devices for the branch circuit. The overload relays protect the motor only.

7.16   A *general-purpose branch circuit* is a circuit that supplies a number of outlets for lighting and appliances. This circuit is typical of the branch circuits found in homes and offices for general lighting and for wall outlets.

7.17   An *individual branch circuit* is a circuit that supplies only one piece of equipment. For example, an individual branch circuit might supply a bench grinder or a single outlet. A duplex receptacle actually consists of two outlets on a single frame, and is therefore not intended for use on an individual branch circuit.

7.18   A *multi-wire branch circuit* is a circuit having two or more ungrounded conductors with a potential difference between them, plus an identified grounded conductor. The potential differences between the grounded conductor and each ungrounded conductor must be equal. In addition, the grounded conductor must be connected to the neutral conductor of the system.

7.19   An example of a multi-wire branch circuit is the familiar 120/240 V single-phase system shown in the upper diagram in Fig. 7-4. The potential difference between the two ungrounded conductors is 240 V. The potential difference between the grounded conductor and each ungrounded conductor is 120 V. The three-phase four-wire circuit is another example of a multi-wire branch circuit. It is shown in the lower diagram in Fig. 7-4. It meets the same basic requirements as the single-phase circuit.

7.20   Article 210.3 of the *NEC* states that branch circuits must be rated in accordance with the maximum permitted ampere rating or setting of the overcurrent device. The rating for other than individual branch circuits must be: 15, 20, 30, 40, and 50 A. If conductors of higher ampacity are used for any reason, the ampere rating or setting of the specified overcurrent device determines the circuit rating.

7.21   This Article means that the conductor must have a current-carrying capacity that is

Fig. 7-4. Multi-wire branch circuits

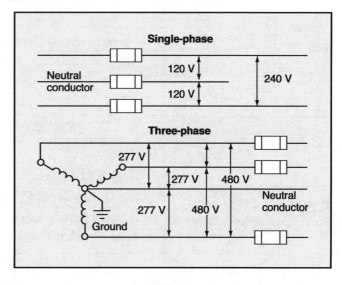

Table 7-1. Circuit protection and conductors for a motor rated at 27 A full-load

Kind of circuit protection	Percentage x 27 =	Maximum current allowable (A)	Maximum rating allowable (A)	Minimum wire size (Copper, THW)
	Table 430.52		Section 240.6	Table 310.15(B)(16)
Nontime-delay fuse.....................	300	81.00	90	No. 8 AWG
Dual-element fuse.....................	175	47.25	50	No. 8 AWG
Instantaneous-trip breaker..............	700	189.00	200	No. 8 AWG
Inverse-time circuit breaker..............	250	67.50	70	No. 8 AWG

not less than the rating or setting of the overcurrent device. However, the size of the conductor does not determine the circuit rating. For example, a circuit wired with No. 10 AWG copper wire is considered a 15 A circuit, even though the wire can carry 30 A safely.

Motor Branch-Circuit Overcurrent Protection

7.22   Looking back to Fig. 7-1, you can see that the next overcurrent protective device is the motor branch-circuit overcurrent protection. This overcurrent protective device may be either a circuit breaker or a fuse. The maximum allowable fuse rating is determined from Table 430.52 in the *NEC*. The motor's full-load current is multiplied by the percentage listed in the table. The percentage is based on the type of motor and its code letter, and on the kind of fuse to be installed.

7.23   For example, a 20 hp motor with code letter H, operating on 480 V, has a full-load current rating of 27 A. The rating of the overload protection depends on what kind of device is installed. The four possibilities are listed in Table 7-1. Notice that the size of the wire does not depend on the kind of overcurrent protection installed. The wire size is based on 125% of the motor's full-load current.

Motor-Running Overcurrent Protection

7.24   Whenever the current rating of a motor is used in determining the ampacity of conductors, switches, or branch-circuit overcurrent devices, the values in *NEC* Tables 430.247 through 430.250 are used instead of the actual current rating marked on the motor nameplate. The selection of motor-running overcurrent protection, however, must be based on the current rating listed on the nameplate.

7.25   The motor-running overcurrent protective device is usually an overload relay. This device is shown just above the motor in Fig. 7-1. The motor overload relay (OL) opens the motor circuit on overloads. Some overload relays do not protect the motor against short circuits. Article 430.40 of the *NEC* requires branch-circuit fuses or circuit breakers in such cases.

7.26   To select overload units for most applications, you must determine the rated full-load current from the motor nameplate. Then you must locate the proper selection tables, based on the class, type, and size of the equipment involved. The proper overload unit number will be found adjacent to the range of full-load currents in which the rated current falls.

7.27   The table for the selection of overload relay units is found on the inside of the motor starter enclosure cover. Tables are also given in the manufacturer's catalog for a particular starter. Always refer to the tables from the manufacturer of the motor starter when selecting overload relay units.

7.28   Thermal overload relays selected from the tables will provide a trip current of 101 to 125% of motor full-load current for many single-speed, normal-torque, 60 Hz motors. Since full-load current ratings of different makes and types of motors vary so much, these selections may not always be suitable. Whenever possible, thermal units should be selected from standard tables on the basis of the full-load currents and service factors listed on the nameplates.

Inherent Thermal Protection

7.29   The last of the protective devices shown in Fig. 7-1 is the *inherent thermal protection*, which senses motor temperature. It is part of the motor's *control* circuit rather than the *power* circuit. Motor current does not flow through this device.

7.30   Motors can fail in many ways. Usually, high temperature does the damage. The life of the insulation on electrical machinery is related directly to temperature. Even with an operator in constant attendance, sudden and dangerous rises in motor temperature may go undetected.

7.31   There are many causes of overheating in motor windings. Some of these include overloading, loss of ventilation, low motor voltage, and too frequent starting. The amount and the rate of temperature rise vary considerably. Proper protective devices respond to the first sudden rise caused by real trouble.

7.32   A reliable way to guard against damaging heat is to provide each motor with built-in temperature-sensing devices. These devices can

Fig. 7-5. Motor-winding thermostat

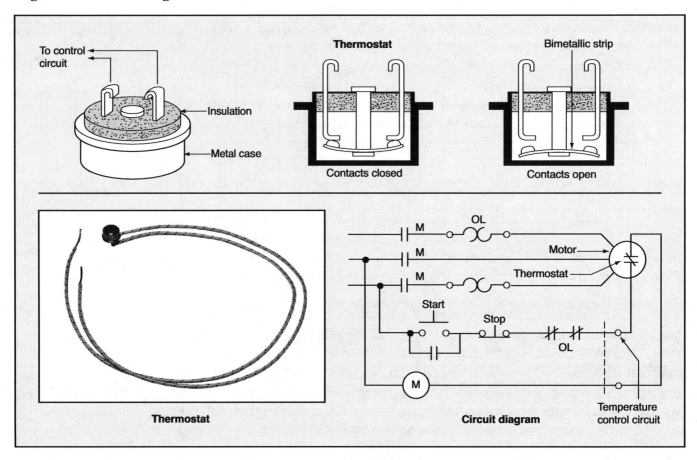

trigger an alarm or take the motor off the line if the temperature rises too high. Specific kinds of devices will be covered in the next section.

7.33   Temperature-monitoring devices are easy to add to existing motors. They are sealed to protect them against dirt and moisture. Whether the device is direct-acting or operates through a remote device, this is the most foolproof way to protect a motor.

Temperature-Sensing Devices

7.34   Protection against overcurrent heating of a motor can be provided either by a *temperature-sensing device* or by a *current-sensing device*. The temperature-sensing device offers better protection than the current-sensing device, because it actually monitors the motor's temperature. Current-sensing devices, including fuses, circuit breakers, relays, and other remote control equipment, protect the power system rather than the motor itself. The motor may overheat because of conditions not detectable by a device installed outside the motor.

7.35   Three kinds of temperature detectors are used in motor windings—*thermostatic*, *resistance*, and *thermocouple*.

7.36   **Thermostatic detectors.** Thermostatic detectors are sealed bimetallic thermostats that are tied securely against the end turns of the motor winding, as close as possible to the "hot spot." This kind of detector has three key characteristics.

- The setting at which the thermostat operates is built in and cannot be adjusted.

- There is only one possible contact arrangement—a single contact that either opens or closes upon a rise in temperature.

- The thermostatic detector gives no indication of the actual temperature or of the rate of rise. All the device tells you is that the winding temperature is somewhere above or below the thermostat's operating point. The control circuit consists only of the thermostat contact in series with a relay that trips the motor breaker.

7.37   One version of the winding thermostat is shown in Fig. 7-5. Notice the action of the bimetallic strip, shown in the internal views. The photograph shows a typical thermostat that would be installed in a motor winding. The circuit diagram shows how the thermostat is connected in the motor-control circuit.

Fig. 7-6. Resistance temperature detector

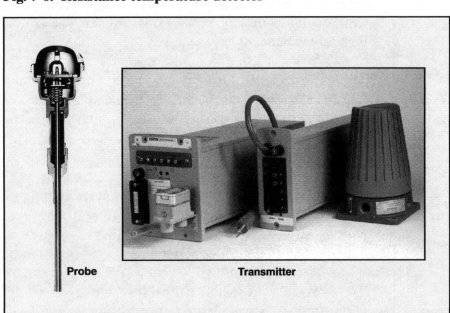

Probe   Transmitter

7.38   Resistance detectors. For large motor windings, the resistance temperature detector, shown in Fig. 7-6 on the previous page, is the most common thermal protective device. The instrument used with this detector is a temperature indicator, not just a switch. It can therefore inform an operator of the actual winding temperature at any time. The probe of the resistance detector is a length of precisely calibrated resistance wire enclosed in a protective shield. It fits through a hole in the motor case, so that it measures the temperature of the motor windings.

7.39   Several resistance detectors are usually provided in a single motor. They are spaced to ensure response to temperature changes in each of the three phases of the winding. Such changes cause corresponding changes in detector wire resistance. These in turn are transmitted to a metering circuit.

7.40   Thermocouple detectors. This kind of temperature detector is similar to the resistance type in appearance and in its location in the motor. However, instead of a resistance wire, its sensing element is a thermocouple, which produces a small potential difference that increases with rising temperature.

7.41   The thermocouple detector can be wired to a remote indicating circuit. However, to avoid extraneous potential differences and incorrect indications, you must use special thermocouple lead wire to connect the detectors into the circuit.

Current-Sensing Devices

7.42   The second kind of device for protection against motor overheating is the current-sensing device. The simplest are fuses and thermal overload relays.

7.43   Fuses. Line fuses provide basic protection for motors. However, line fuses have a disadvantage in that they act only under conditions of excess current. An increase in winding temperature from a cause other than current can result in the windings overheating without receiving any protection from the fuse.

7.44   Motors require much more current for starting than for running. In many cases, the starting-current surge may be three to six times the normal running current. An ordinary line fuse blows very quickly if the current exceeds the rating of the fuse.

7.45   You could install a line fuse having a rating high enough to permit the necessary starting current. But such a fuse would give little

Fig. 7-7. Protected three-phase motor circuit

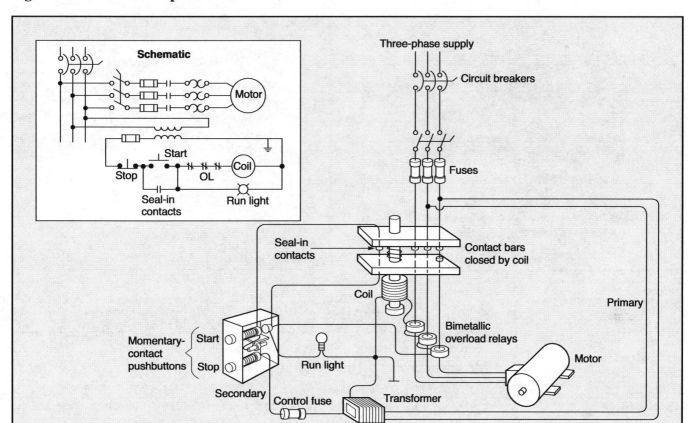

or no protection against overheating of the windings under normal running-load current conditions. Line fuses are also inadequate as protection for the motor, because they are easily replaceable with a fuse of a higher rating. For example, if the load current becomes high enough to blow the fuse, it is a simple matter to substitute a fuse with a higher rating. But the motor windings can be damaged if the overload continues.

7.46   Thermal time-delay fuses are now widely used. One kind, known as the *dual-element fuse,* has a time delay that holds the current-carrying element while the motor starts. Yet, the fuse provides the same overcurrent protection as an ordinary fuse.

7.47   **Thermal overload relays.** Most motor burnouts are caused by currents that exceed the motor's rating. In the thermal OL relay, excessive current raises the temperature of a heater element. The increased temperature actuates the relay, which trips a latch and opens the motor-control circuit to disconnect the motor from the line. A simple diagram of a protected motor circuit is shown in Fig. 7-7. The schematic diagram shows how the parts function together.

Fig. 7-8. Overload relays on a motor starter

Overload relays

Fig. 7-9. Overload relays and heaters

7.48   For reliable operation, the overload relay must be located in the same temperature environment as the motor. The safety factor that represents the motor's protection is the difference between the overload trip temperature and the motor insulating rating.

7.49   As the ambient temperature rises, less load current is needed to trip the relay. In cool surroundings, the opposite effect occurs—the motor runs cooler and is capable of carrying a higher load current without overheating. At the same time, the overload relay will handle a higher current without tripping. Under these conditions, the maximum load a motor can safely carry closely parallels the maximum current the overload relay will allow it to carry. This is an ideal match for open-type motors operating at the same ambient temperature as the overload relay.

7.50   Overload tripping may occur under high ambient-temperature conditions. It is then tempting to conclude that this is a nuisance trip, and to make an effort to prevent the relay from operating. Replacing the correct heater element with a larger one is poor practice. It reduces the motor protection at all temperatures. Trip-free relays are available and should be specified on all motor controls. A *trip-free relay* will trip even if the reset pusher is blocked or held in.

7.51   A heater element in the relay is connected in series with the motor circuit. Tripping is accomplished by the relay, which opens the motor-control circuit. The trip point (measured in amperes) is determined by the heater rating. Figure 7-8 shows an example of a motor starter with three thermal overload relays attached.

Fig. 7-10. Melting-alloy relay

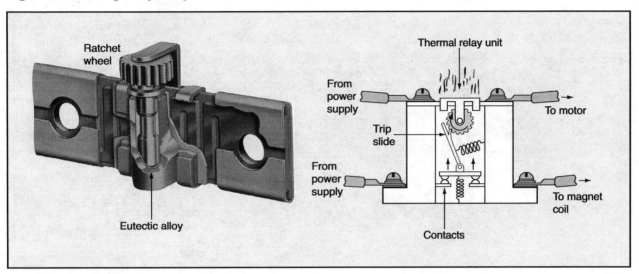

7.52   Heaters of various current ratings are interchangeable within the specific product lines of any given manufacturer. The appearances of heaters vary greatly from one manufacturer to another, and even among different lines offered by the same manufacturer. However, all heaters translate an increase in motor current to an increase in temperature in the overload relay. Some examples of heaters are shown in Fig. 7-9.

Melting-Alloy Relays

7.53   In a melting-alloy overload relay, the heating element melts a metal alloy inside the relay. The alloy is selected to melt at a precise temperature, usually near 100°C (212°F). When the alloy melts, it allows a plunger to rotate, releasing a spring-loaded trip slide, as shown in Fig. 7-10.

7.54   A *eutectic alloy* melts at a precise temperature, and goes directly from solid to liquid stage. There is no "soft" stage between the liquid and solid stages. The temperature at which the alloy melts is not affected by time or use. When the alloy refreezes after tripping, the plunger can no longer rotate, and you can reset the spring-loaded relay contacts.

7.55   Generally, this kind of overload relay has high contact forces and is shock-resistant. Its contacts can withstand high inrush and continuous currents, and the unit is practically waterproof. These relays are considered to be the most reliable of all thermal overload protective devices.

Fig. 7-11. Bimetallic relay

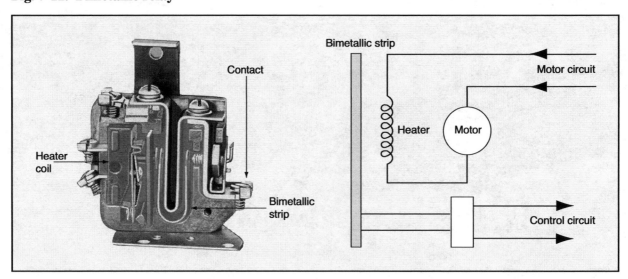

7.56   Melting-alloy relays are also called *solder-pot relays*. This name comes from the fact that solder is an alloy (of tin and lead). However, ordinary solder is never used in melting-alloy relays. The melting point of the alloy is fixed by the alloy's composition, and it cannot be adjusted. These relays have trip indicators to provide visible evidence of tripping. Melting-alloy relays require no calibration.

Bimetallic Relays

7.57   Bimetallic overload relays work on another principle. Figure 7-11 is a diagram of this kind of relay. Heat causes the bimetallic strip to bend, because the two metals expand at different rates. As the heater current increases, the bimetallic strip bends until it actuates a switch.

7.58   Often, bimetallic relays can be adjusted for either automatic or manual reset. The bimetallic strip is able to trip the switch during heating, and is strong enough to trip the switch back again during cooling. Thus, the relay can reset automatically.

7.59   Variations in individual bimetallic relays make it necessary for them to be calibrated during manufacture. This is done by means of an adjustment screw that sets the relay to trip at a precise temperature, generally near 100 °C (approximately 200°F). After adjustment, the screw is sealed to prevent tampering.

7.60   All the overload relays discussed so far have one major limitation. They do not directly sense the motor temperature. Most relays are designed to operate by paralleling the motor temperature, and they do a

Fig. 7-12. Temperatures from intermittent load

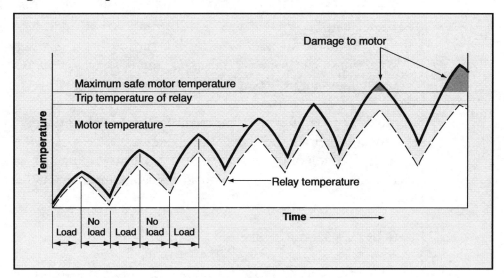

fairly accurate job under both steady running conditions and widely fluctuating conditions.

7.61   If a motor starts and stops often, however, it may not be completely protected by the bimetallic relay. The graph in Fig. 7-12 shows why. As the motor is loaded, the relay temperature parallels the motor temperature closely. But when the motor is off, the relay cools faster than the motor because it has less mass. After operating through several cycles, the temperature of the relay may be much lower than that of the motor. Thus, the motor may become too hot, but the overload relay will not have reached its trip point.

7.62   The relay and the motor will again operate at corresponding temperatures if the operating cycle changes in one of two ways.

- If the motor remains off for a long-enough time, both the motor and the relay will cool to the surrounding temperature.

- If the motor remains on for a long-enough time, both the motor and the relay will rise to the same temperature.

7.63   The *National Electrical Code* defines the upper limit on the rating of a motor overload protector. The protective device must trip at no more than 125% of the motor's full-load current rating, depending on the kind of motor.

7.64   In determining how heaters will be rated in their respective lines, manufacturers use different methods for ensuring that *NEC* requirements are met for all motors. Although the methods of rating heaters differ among manufacturers, the results are the same.

7.65   Overload heaters are rated in current increments of about 10%. About 50 heaters are required to span the range from 0.5 to 50 A. Each heater can be applied over a 10% range of current. The manufacturer supplies heater-selection tables indicating the range for various conditions. The heater's "must-trip" rating (specified in amperes) is 125% of the minimum value of the full-load current range.

7.66   Among the most important factors to be considered in selecting the proper heater are the ambient temperatures at the location of the motor and at the location of the protective device. Heater trip ratings, as well as ratings of today's motors, are based on an ambient temperature of 40°C (105°F).

Selecting Motor Protection

7.67   Article 430.6(A)(2) of the *National Electrical Code* states that "Separate motor overload protection shall be based on the motor nameplate current rating." In the same Article (430) of the Code, however, tables give nominal full-load current for motors of various horsepower ratings. In the past, it was a common practice to select overload protection entirely on the basis of current ratings given in these tables. Unfortunately, this practice is still followed in many plants today.

7.68   Good practice calls for a policy of specifying motor protection on the basis of actual motor characteristics. Such a policy means that protection will be selected on the basis of motor nameplate information, rather than on a table that gives nominal characteristics for a broad class of motors.

7.69   Because of differences in basic design, speed, efficiency, and power factor, motors having identical horsepower ratings can have quite different current ratings. A heater selected on the basis of the *NEC* tables, rather than on the basis of the motor's nameplate rating, can trip the relay at a current that is significantly too high or too low. Using nominal standards to select the heater for a specific motor always involves a certain amount of unnecessary risk.

7.70   Selection of proper overload heaters is essential to providing proper protection. It is because of improper heater selection that most thermal OL relays are used improperly. There are two ways to select the right heater.

- The motor manufacturer provides a list of the approved heaters to be used with the motor under various environmental conditions.

- The heater is selected at the job site, where the nameplate information is read firsthand.

7.71   In addition to the full-load current rating, motor nameplate information is helpful in selecting the proper heater. Article 430.32(A)(l) of the *NEC* states that motors with a service factor lower than 1.15 must be protected by an overcurrent device rated to trip at not more than 115% of the motor's rated full-load current. A service factor of 1.15 means that the manufacturer guarantees successful operation at 1.15 times the rated full-load current without damage due to heating.

7.72   However, the service factor can be other than 1.15. Motor manufacturers list the value on the motor nameplate. Because OL relay heater elements are rated in 10% increments, it is important to select a heater only one size smaller. This reduction decreases the protection margin from the standard 125% of motor rating to the required 115%.

7.73   Nearly all motors classified by the National Electrical Manufacturers Association (NEMA) as TEFC (totally enclosed, fan cooled) motors, with Class B insulation, have a service factor of 1.0. These motors must be protected according to the 115 percent standard.

7.74   Article 430.32(A)(1) of the *NEC* also states that motors rated for a temperature rise in excess of 40°C must also be protected at a maximum of 115% of full load rating. For such motors, the next smaller heater must also be selected from the relay manufacturer's heater selection table.

7.75   It is good practice to follow the 115% rule any time the service factor cannot be identified as being 1.15 or higher. Use the same rule if you cannot identify the temperature rise as being a maximum of 40°C.

Ambient-Compensated Overload Relays

7.76   Where the ambient temperature at the relay requires a heater rated two sizes larger than the one specified by the manufacturer's tables, you should use an ambient-compensated OL relay. An increase in heater size alters the overall trip characteristics of the relay. If heaters two or more sizes over the basic recommendation are installed, the change in trip characteristics can become significant. Using compensating-type relays eliminates the need for heater derating.

7.77   Melting-alloy and bimetallic thermal overload relays are not completely reliable when the motor is operating in a constant temperature and the relay is operating in varying temperatures. Ambient temperature affects both kinds of relays, but not the motor. Therefore, it is best to use an overload relay that reacts only to the motor current and not to changes in ambient temperature. Figure 7-13, on the following page, shows the effect

Fig. 7-13. Comparison of relays

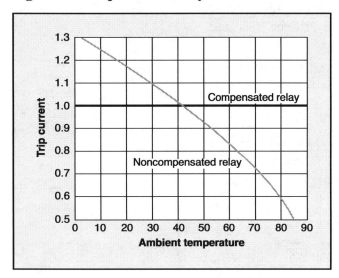

of ambient temperature on the ultimate trip current of both compensated and noncompensated relays.

7.78   The diagram in Fig. 7-14 shows how a compensated relay works. The main bimetallic strip is fixed at one end and receives the heat from the heater above it. The compensating bimetallic strip is riveted to a trip lever. A flat spring acts as a pivot and forces both bimetallic strips to bear against the spacer at points A and B. This force also holds the lever properly against the toggle switch, which is fixed in position.

7.79   An increase in ambient temperature causes both bimetallic strips to bend downward equally. Thus, the lever does not change position, and the toggle switch does not operate. However, an increase in current in the heater element bends the main bimetallic strip without affecting the compensating strip. The spacer pushes the lower bimetallic strip downward. The lower strip pivots on the flat spring. At this point, the lever operates the toggle switch.

7.80   Ambient-compensated bimetallic overload relays are available for either automatic or manual reset. Their tripping currents and times are independent of ambient temperatures within a range of -29 to 77°C (-20 to 170°F). Most of these relays are designed to be trip-free. Like the noncompensated relays, a well-designed compensated relay has contacts that are self-cleaning. They wipe as the bimetallic strips deflect.

Fig. 7-14. Temperature-compensated relay

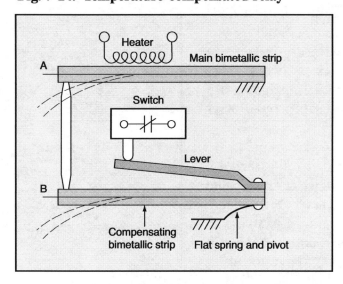

Single Phasing

7.81   It is not unusual for three-phase motors to continue running after one phase has been lost. This condition is commonly called *single phasing*. An open phase in the primary of a Y-delta or delta-Y transformer serving a motor causes approximately twice the rated current to appear in one phase of the motor if the motor continues to run. If the phase carrying the high current lacks overcurrent protection, as shown in Fig. 7-15, the single-phasing motor can be seriously damaged.

7.82   It was previously thought that protection in only two phases was adequate, because it is unlikely that all factors leading to this unprotected condition will be present. However, Table 430.37 of the *National Electrical Code* requires OL protection in all three phases of a three-phase system. Manufacturers now include protection in the third phase.

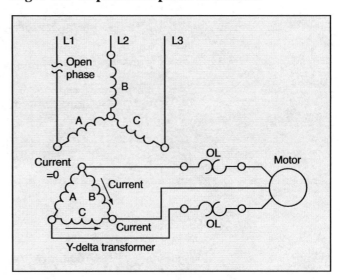

Fig. 7-15. **Unprotected phase in a motor**

Protecting Overload Relays

7.83   No discussion of the application of thermal overload relays for motor protection is complete without considering protection for the relay itself. Overload relays and their heater elements are designed to withstand current somewhat in excess of the locked-rotor currents of the motors they are intended to protect. However, if fault currents exceeding 13 times the motor's full-load current rating occur, and proper motor branch circuit protection has not been provided, the heater will be damaged.

7.84   Fault currents exceeding 100 times a motor's full-load current rating are not unusual. If such a condition occurs, the heater can act as a fuse. With the heater not conducting—and therefore not heating—the relay itself, as well as the motor it is intended to protect, can be seriously damaged.

7.85   Table 430.7(B) in the *NEC* defines letter codes based on the electrical power (measured in kilovolt-amperes) drawn by a motor, per horsepower of rated mechanical power, when the rotor is locked. The maximum size of a motor branch circuit protector is then defined in Table 430.52, as a multiple of the motor's full-load current based on these code letters.

7.86   The maximum allowed rating of any protective device depends on the particular kind of device it is. For example, the allowed rating of an instantaneous-trip circuit breaker is generally four to five times the rating allowed for a dual-element fuse. The branch-circuit protector must be capable of operating at a current greater than the locked-rotor current and less than 13 times the motor's full-load current.

7.87   The wide use of thermal overload relays indicates their acceptance as the most practical means of providing overload protection for motors. Proper heater selection is the key to proper application of thermal overload relays. Therefore, you must pay careful attention to the factors that affect heater performance. Most significant among these factors are the following:

- full-load current

- temperature-rise rating

- service factor

- ambient temperature, at the motor and at the protector

- locked-rotor current ratio

- starting time

- duty cycle

- locked-rotor endurance time.

If these factors are not considered, the result is poor relay performance.

Contributions from the following sources are appreciated:

Figure 1-4.	Square D Company
Figure 1-5.	Square D Company
Figure 2-1.	Encon
Figure 2-2.	W. H Salisbury
Figure 2-3.	Norton Company—Safety Products Division
Figure 2-4.	Norton Company—Safety Products Division & Cabot Safety Corporation
Figure 2-5.	Bradley Washfountain Company
Figure 2-6.	American Ed-Co., Inc. IDEAL INDUSTRIES, INC.
Figure 2-7.	American Allsafe Co.
Figure 2-8.	Cementex Products, Inc.
Figure 2-9.	Hubbell Power Systems/Chance
Figure 3-1.	IDEAL INDUSTRIES, INC.
Figure 3-2.	ED-CO Lockouts and Padlocks
Figure 3-3.	Harvey Hubbell, Inc.
Figure 4-2.	®The Boeing Company.
Figure 4-7.	Siemens
Figure 5-1.	Harvey Hubbell, Inc.
Figure 5-7.	Square D Company
Figure 6-1.	Bussman Div., McGraw-Edison Co.
Figure 6-2.	GC Electronics
Figure 6-3.	Reliance Fuse, Div. of Federal Pacific Electric
Figure 6-5.	Reliance Fuse, Div. of Federal Pacific Electric
Figure 6-6.	Reliance Fuse, Div. of Federal Pacific Electric
Figure 6-7.	McGraw-Edison Company, Power Systems Group
Figure 6-8.	Bussman Mfg. Div., McGraw-Edison Co.
Figure 6-9.	Reliance Fuse, Div. of Federal Pacific Electric
Figure 6-10.	Reliance Fuse, Div. of Federal Pacific Electric
Figure 6-11.	Bussman Mfg. Div., McGraw-Edison Co.
Figure 6-12.	Bussman Mfg. Div., McGraw-Edison Co.
Figure 6-16.	Gould Inc., Distribution & Controls Div.
Figure 6-17.	Gould Inc., Distribution & Controls Div.
Figure 6-18.	Reliance Electric, Div. of Federal Pacific
Figure 6-19.	Reliance Electric, Div. of Federal Pacific
Figure 7-5.	The Foxboro Company
Figure 7-8.	Ward Leonard Electric Co., Inc.
Figure 7-9.	Ward Leonard Electric Co., Inc.
Figure 7-10.	Square D Company
Figure 7-11.	Square D Company